D1201045

Presented to the
Ironside Memorial Library
Bryan College
WITHDRAWN
by
William M. Swyter

Vectors and Their Applications

TEACHERS' MATHEMATICS REFERENCE SERIES

Bruce E. Meserve, Series Editor

Hight	A CONCEPT OF LIMITS
Parker	THE STRUCTURE OF NUMBER SYSTEMS
Pettofrezzo	VECTORS AND THEIR APPLICATIONS
Smith	EXPLORATIONS IN ELEMENTARY MATHEMATICS

PRENTICE-HALL INTERNATIONAL, INC., London
PRENTICE-HALL OF AUSTRALIA, PTY., LTD., Sydney
PRENTICE-HALL OF CANADA, LTD., Toronto
PRENTICE-HALL OF INDIA (PRIVATE) LTD., New Delhi
PRENTICE-HALL OF JAPAN, LTD., Tokyo

Anthony J. Pettofrezzo

Associate Professor of Mathematics
Montclair State College, New Jersey

VECTORS AND THEIR APPLICATIONS

PRENTICE-HALL, INC., ENGLEWOOD CLIFFS, NEW JERSEY

To Betty

Library of Congress Catalog Card Number:
66–10185

Printed in the United States of America
C-94143

Series Foreword

Each book of this series is concerned with an important topic or area of the mathematical training of teachers. The exposition follows the highly successful pattern of the Meserve-Sobel books. There are many illustrative examples to facilitate the use of the books for individual study and in-service programs. There are numerous exercises to provide an opportunity for readers to develop their understanding. The answers for the odd-numbered exercises are in the back of each book; the answers for the even-numbered exercises are available in a separate booklet. Thus each book is designed to serve as a text either in an in-service program or in a college course for prospective teachers or others interested in extending their knowledge of these mathematical concepts. Some of the books are particularly useful as supplementary texts in college and advanced high-school courses.

The topics for these books have been selected because of their significance in the rapid evolution of our contemporary mathematics curricula. Each author has tested his materials in preliminary form with hundreds and (in at least one case) thousands of college students and/or school teachers. Briefly, this series consists of books on significant topics presenting tested materials in a manner that has been proved to be highly effective.

The brevity of the books is purposeful. Each book may be used as a supplementary reference text in a more extensive or advanced course. Each book provides the basis for an extensive unit of work in an in-service, college, or school course. Considerable flexibility in meeting the needs of the students is available by using two or more of these books in an extensive course or series of courses.

Frequent additions of books to this series are contemplated.

Bruce E. Meserve, Series Editor

Preface

THE CONCEPT of a vector is of fundamental importance to the study of many areas of advanced mathematics and the physical sciences. A study of geometric vectors of two-and three-dimensional space is an aid toward the understanding of abstract vector spaces, matrices, tensors, and other multicomponent algebras. The purpose of this book is to familiarize the reader with those concepts of vector algebra that have applications to algebra, geometry, trigonometry, and physics.

Vector algebra is developed as an algebra of directed line segments. The motivation of ideas and definitions are included wherever appropriate. Particular attention has been paid to the formulation of precise definitions and statements of theorems. Coordinate position vectors are treated. The key concepts necessary for the study of generalized vector spaces are presented and developed.

The main theme throughout the book is the use of vectors as a mathematical tool in the study of elementary plane and solid geometry, plane and spherical trigonometry, and coordinate geometry. Many theorems of elementary mathematics have simple and elegant vector proofs, which are illustrated in detail in this book.

More than the usual number of illustrative examples have been included as an aid to the reader in his mastery of the concepts presented. There are a sufficient number of exercises, which either supplement the theory presented or give the reader an opportunity to reinforce his understanding of the applications. Answers are provided to the odd-numbered exercises; the answers to the even-numbered exercises are available in a separate booklet.

With the development of the modern mathematics programs in the high schools, it is believed that this book will fill the need of many teachers and prospective teachers for a background in vector algebra. The many illustrative examples make the book quite useful for individual study and in-service programs. This book contains enough material for a semester course at the high-school or college level.

There are many people to whom I am indebted for the completion and publication of this book. A debt of gratitude is acknowledged to Dr. Bruce E. Meserve of the University of Vermont, who read the manuscript for this book at various stages of its development, for his suggestions, constructive criticisms, and encouragement. To those students of Montclair State College who studied the preliminary versions of this material, a special thanks. I wish to express my appreciation to my wife, Betty, not only for typing the manuscript, but for her patience and understanding. Finally, I wish to thank the editorial staff of Prentice-Hall, Inc., for their kind cooperation.

Anthony J. Pettofrezzo

Contents

Vectors and Their Applications

chapter 1

Elementary Operations

1-1 Scalars and Vectors

In discussing physical space it is necessary to consider several types of physical quantities. One class of quantities consists of those quantities which have associated with them some measure of undirected magnitude. Such quantities are called *scalar quantities* or simply *scalars*. Each scalar quantity can be represented by a real number which indicates the magnitude of the quantity according to some arbitrarily chosen convenient scale or unit of measure. Since scalars are real numbers, scalars enter into combinations according to the rules of the algebra of real numbers. Mass, density, area, volume, time, work, electrical charge, potential, temperature, and population are examples of scalar quantities.

A second class of physical quantities consists of those quantities which have associated with them both the property of magnitude and the property of direction. Such quantities are called *vector quantities* or simply *vectors*. Force, velocity, acceleration, and momentum are examples of vector quantities.

The following example illustrates the need to distinguish between scalars and vectors. Consider a plane which flies from point A to point B, 300 miles east of A, and then proceeds to fly north to a third point C, 400 miles north of B as shown in Figure 1–1. The distances which the plane has flown are scalars and may be added in the usual manner to determine the total distance covered by the flight; that is, $300 + 400$, or 700, miles. The flight may also be considered in terms of the displacement of the plane from point A to point C.

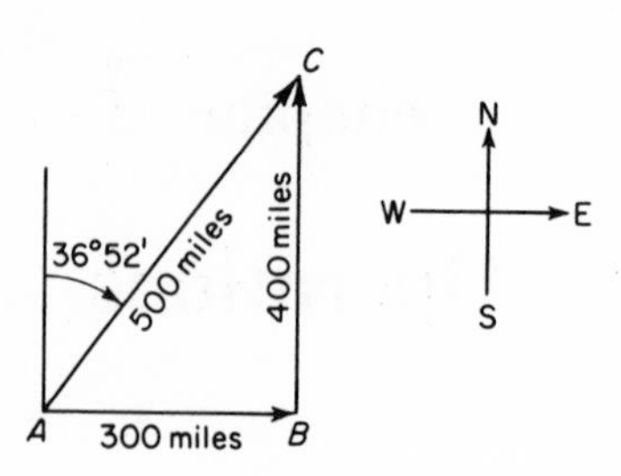

Figure 1-1

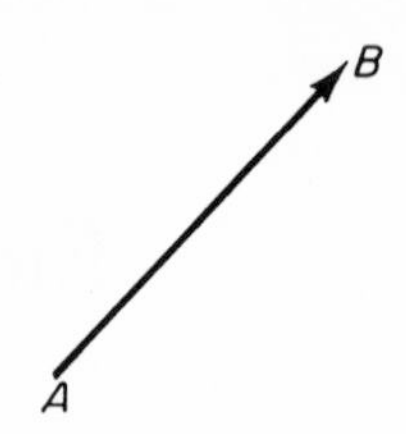

Figure 1-2

This displacement may be considered as the sum of two displacements: one 300 miles east from A to B and the second 400 miles north from B to C; the sum of these displacements is the displacement 500 miles with a bearing of approximately 36°52′ east of north from A to C. Notice that direction as well as magnitude is considered in describing displacements. Displacements are examples of vector quantities. Furthermore, the sum of two displacements is calculated in a rather different manner than the sum of two scalar quantities; in other words, vector addition is quite different from scalar addition.

Notice that in Figure 1-1 the displacements were denoted by means of directed line segments or arrows. In mathematics it is convenient to construct a geometric model of the physical concept of a vector and of situations involving vector quantities.

Definition 1-1 *A geometric vector or simply a* ***vector*** *is a directed line segment (Figure 1-2).*

In Figure 1-2 the length of the directed line segment with reference to some conveniently chosen unit of length is associated with the magnitude of the vector; thus, lengths of directed line segments represent scalars. Notice that the magnitude of a vector is a non-negative real number. Unless otherwise restricted, we shall consider a geometric vector as a vector in three-dimensional space.

The notation for a vector which we shall use is due to the mathematician Argand. Symbolically the vector represented in Figure 1-2 is denoted by $\overrightarrow{AB}$, where A is the **initial point** (sometimes called the **origin** or **origin point**) of the directed line segment and B is the **terminal point**. Symbolically the magnitude of $\overrightarrow{AB}$ is denoted by $|\overrightarrow{AB}|$. Whenever convenient, a second notation for vectors will be used, which consists of single small letters beneath a half arrow such as $\vec{a}, \vec{b}, \vec{c}, \ldots$. Then $|\vec{a}|, |\vec{b}|, |\vec{c}|, \ldots$ will represent the magnitudes of such vectors.

In our study of vectors we shall often "associate" a vector with a line segment. It is possible to associate either $\overrightarrow{AB}$ or $\overrightarrow{BA}$ with the line segment whose end points are A and B, where in each case the magnitude of the vector is equal to the length of the line segment. However, the vectors $\overrightarrow{AB}$ and $\overrightarrow{BA}$ are not equal. When we use the second notation of a single small letter to represent a vector associated with a line segment, we will find it convenient to adopt the following convention for establishing the association we desire: "*associate* $\vec{a}$ *with line segment* AB" *shall mean* $\vec{a} = \overrightarrow{AB}$; "*associate* $\vec{a}$ *with line segment* BA" *shall mean* $\vec{a} = \overrightarrow{BA}$. Note that line segments AB and BA are identical and thus that our convention is strictly a notational procedure for this book.

A vector of particular interest is the zero vector or null vector, which will be denoted by $\vec{0}$.

Definition 1-2 *A* ***null vector*** *is a vector whose magnitude is zero.*

By Definition 1-2, a geometric vector is a null vector if its initial and terminal points coincide. We choose to consider a null vector as a vector without a unique direction and, specifically, with a direction that is indeterminate. The null vector is the only vector whose direction is indeterminate. Some mathematicians choose to consider the null vector as having any arbitrary direction; that is, a null vector could be considered as the limit of any one of an infinite number of finite vectors as its magnitude approaches zero. The wording of many theorems in the subsequent development of vector algebra must be carefully changed if the direction of the null vector is considered arbitrary.

Exercises

Identify each quantity as either a scalar quantity or a vector quantity.

1. Distance between New York and Boston.

2. Displacement from Chicago to St. Louis.

3. Temperature of 97° Fahrenheit.

4. Weight of 100 pounds.

5. Pressure of 18 pounds per square inch.

6. 250 horsepower.

1-2 Equality of Vectors

In choosing an appropriate definition for the equality of two vectors one is usually guided by the applications that will be made of the vectors. For example, in the study of the theory of mechanics of rigid bodies, vectors $\vec{a}$ and $\vec{b}$ (denoting forces) have the same mechanical effect, in that the "line of action" of these two vectors is the same and the vectors have the same magnitude. However, as in Figure 1-3, the mechanical effect of $\vec{c}$, a vector of equal magnitude to $\vec{a}$ and $\vec{b}$, would be to rotate the shaded object acted upon. In this type of problem $\vec{a}$ and $\vec{b}$ would be considered equal since they have equal magnitudes and lie along the same line with the same orientation. Consideration of this type of problem requires a definition of equality for a class of vectors commonly called **line vectors.**

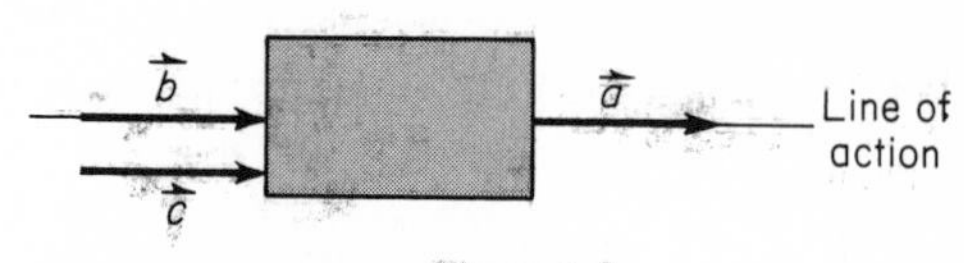

Figure 1-3

In the theory of mechanics of deformable bodies one needs a more restrictive definition for the equality of vectors. For example, consider $\vec{a}$ and $\vec{b}$, both having equal magnitudes and directed along the same line with the same orientation, acting upon an elastic material as indicated in Figure 1-4. Each vector would deform the material in a different way; $\vec{a}$ would tend to compress it, while $\vec{b}$ would tend to stretch it. A consideration of this type of problem leads to a definition for the equality of vectors: vectors with equal magnitudes and acting along the same line of action with the same orientation are to be applied at the same point in space. A study of vectors under this definition of equality is a study of **bound vectors**.

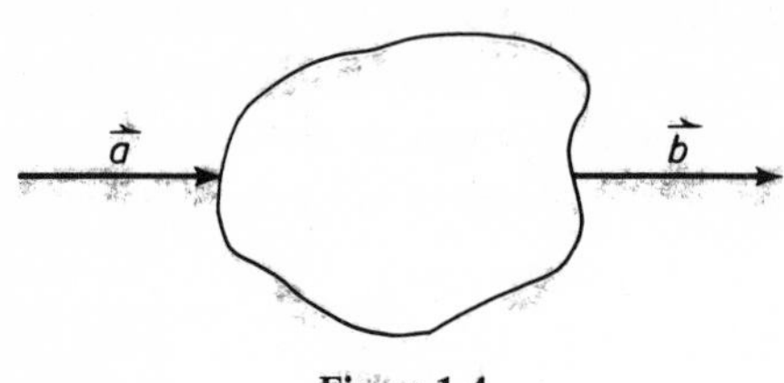

Figure 1-4

However, those properties of geometry and trigonometry with which one is generally interested in mathematics, allow mathematicians to use a less restrictive definition for the equality of vectors.

Definition 1-3 *Two vectors $\vec{a}$ and $\vec{b}$ are* ***equal*** *if, and only if, $|\vec{a}| = |\vec{b}|$ and $\vec{a}$ is parallel to $\vec{b}$ with the same orientation; that is, $\vec{a} = \vec{b}$ if, and only if, $\vec{a}$ and $\vec{b}$ have the same magnitude and direction.*

In Definition 1-3 the word "parallel" is used in a generalized sense to mean that the vectors are on the same or parallel lines; "orientation" refers to the "sense" of the vector along the line; "direction" refers to both parallelism and orientation. From the definition it follows that any vector may be subjected to a parallel displacement without considering its magnitude or direction as being changed. The vectors in Figure 1-5 are all equal to one another. Since the vectors are equal, any one of the vectors may be considered to represent a whole class of equal vectors of which the others are members.

Under Definition 1-3 for the equality of vectors, the vectors discussed are called **free vectors**. Unless otherwise specified, we shall assume that all vectors are free vectors.

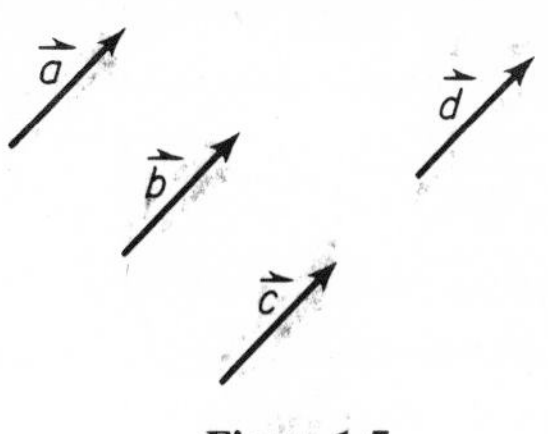

Figure 1-5

Exercises

In Exercises 1 through 6 state whether or not the two vectors appear to be equal.

1.

2.

3.

4.

5.

6.

In Exercises 7 through 9 copy the given figure and draw a vector with the given point P as its initial point and equal to the given vector.

7. •P

8. P

9. 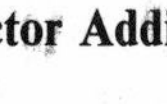 P

10–12. Copy the given figure in Exercises 7 through 9 and draw a vector with the given point P as its terminal point and equal to the given vector.

1-3 Vector Addition and Subtraction

Consideration of the displacement problem of § 1-1 and similar physical problems concerning vectors motivated the following definition called the **law of vector addition**.

Definition 1-4 *Given two vectors $\vec{a}$ and $\vec{b}$, if $\vec{b}$ is translated so that its initial point coincides with the terminal point of $\vec{a}$, then a third vector $\vec{c}$ with the same initial point as $\vec{a}$ and the same terminal point as $\vec{b}$ is equal to $\vec{a} + \vec{b}$ (Figure 1-6).*

The sum of two vectors is a uniquely determined vector; that is, if $\vec{c} = \vec{a} + \vec{b}$ and $\vec{d} = \vec{a} + \vec{b}$, then $\vec{c} = \vec{d}$.

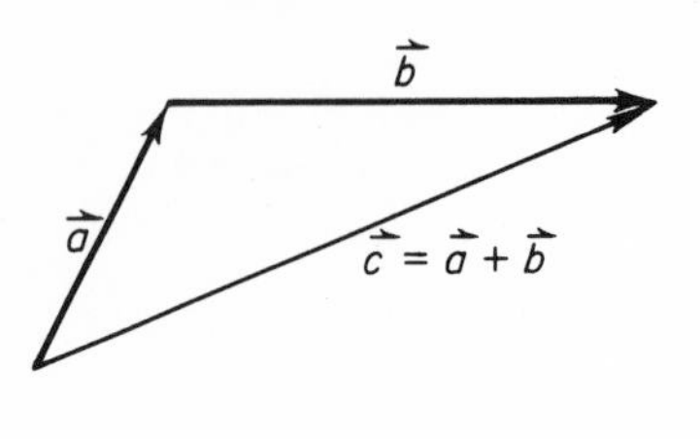

Figure 1-6

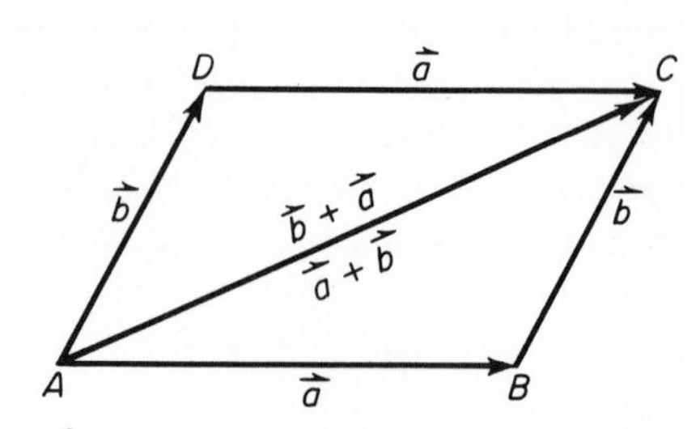

Figure 1-7

Consider any parallelogram $ABCD$. Associate vectors $\vec{a}$ and $\vec{b}$ with sides AB and BC, respectively, as in Figure 1-7. Then $\vec{a} + \vec{b}$ may be associated with the diagonal AC. Since the opposite sides of any parallelogram are equal and parallel, $\vec{b}$ and $\vec{a}$ may be associated with sides AD and DC, respectively. By Definition 1-4, $\vec{b} + \vec{a}$ may also be associated with the diagonal AC. Hence, one of the fundamental properties of the addition of real numbers is also valid for the addition of vectors.

Theorem 1-1 *Vector addition is commutative; that is,*

$$\vec{a} + \vec{b} = \vec{b} + \vec{a}. \tag{1-1}$$

The law of vector addition is sometimes called the **triangle law of addition** or the **parallelogram law of addition**. A consideration of Figures 1-6 and 1-7 motivated the use of these terms.

Associativity is another familiar property of the addition of real numbers that also holds for the addition of vectors.

Theorem 1-2 *Vector addition is associative; that is,*

$$\vec{a} + (\vec{b} + \vec{c}) = (\vec{a} + \vec{b}) + \vec{c}. \tag{1-2}$$

Proof: Consider a parallelepiped $ABCDEFGH$. Associate with sides AB, AD, and AE vectors $\vec{a}$, $\vec{b}$, and $\vec{c}$, respectively, as in Figure 1-8. Then,

$$\overrightarrow{AG} = \overrightarrow{AH} + \overrightarrow{HG} \text{ and } \overrightarrow{AG} = \overrightarrow{AC} + \overrightarrow{CG}. \qquad \text{(Def. 1-4)}$$

Therefore,

$$\overrightarrow{HG} + \overrightarrow{AH} = \overrightarrow{AC} + \overrightarrow{CG} \qquad \text{(Theorem 1-1)}$$

$$\overrightarrow{HG} + (\overrightarrow{AD} + \overrightarrow{DH}) = (\overrightarrow{AB} + \overrightarrow{BC}) + \overrightarrow{CG} \qquad \text{(Def. 1-4)}$$

$$\overrightarrow{AB} + (\overrightarrow{AD} + \overrightarrow{AE}) = (\overrightarrow{AB} + \overrightarrow{AD}) + \overrightarrow{AE}. \qquad \text{(Def. 1-3)}$$

Hence,

$$\vec{a} + (\vec{b} + \vec{c}) = (\vec{a} + \vec{b}) + \vec{c}.$$

The associative property of vector addition may be extended to find the sum of more than three vectors. If the initial point of each succeeding vector is placed at the terminal point of the preceding one, then that vector with the same initial point as the first vector and the same terminal point as the last vector represents the sum of the vectors.

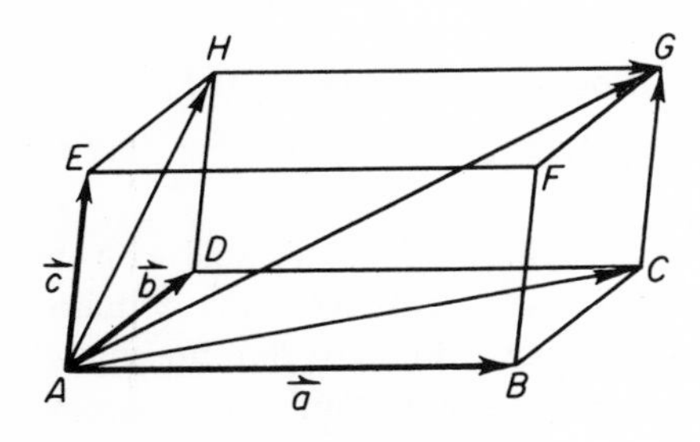

Figure 1-8

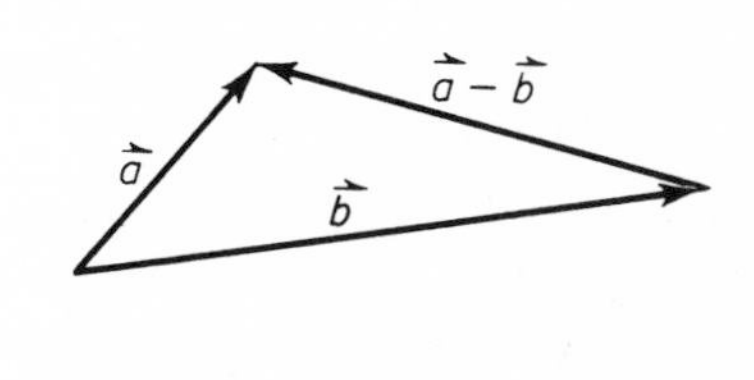

Figure 1-9

Definition 1-5 *If two vectors $\vec{a}$ and $\vec{b}$ have a common initial point, then their difference $\vec{a} - \vec{b}$ is the vector $\vec{c}$ extending from the terminal point of $\vec{b}$ to the terminal point of $\vec{a}$ (Figure 1-9).*

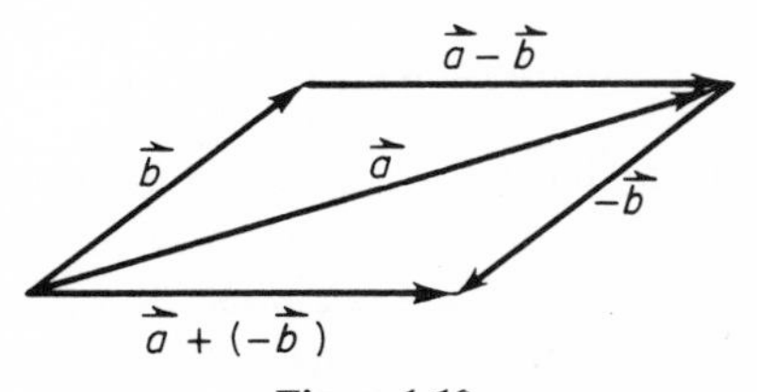

Figure 1-10

If $\vec{b} = \vec{a}$, then $\vec{a} - \vec{a} = \vec{0}$, the null vector. Furthermore, if $-\vec{b}$ is used to represent a vector equal in magnitude to $\vec{b}$ but having the opposite direction from $\vec{b}$, then $\vec{a} - \vec{b} = \vec{a} + (-\vec{b})$ as shown in Figure 1-10.

Exercises

1. Simplify: (a) $\overrightarrow{AB} + \overrightarrow{BC} + \overrightarrow{CD}$; (b) $\overrightarrow{RS} + \overrightarrow{ST} + \overrightarrow{TU} + \overrightarrow{UR}$.
2. Simplify: (a) $\overrightarrow{AB} - \overrightarrow{CB}$;
   (b) $\overrightarrow{MN} - \overrightarrow{RP} - \overrightarrow{PN}$.
3. Use geometric constructions to copy the coplanar vectors in the figure, and show that the sum of the vectors appears to be a null vector.

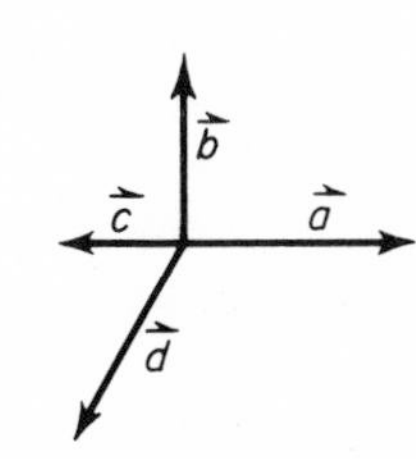

4. If $\vec{a}$ and $\vec{b}$ are vectors associated with adjacent sides AB and BC of a regular hexagon $ABCDEF$, determine vectors which may be associated with the other four sides CD, DE, EF, and FA.

5. Prove that $(\vec{a} + \vec{b}) + \vec{c} = (\vec{c} + \vec{a}) + \vec{b}$ by using Theorems 1-1 and 1-2.

6. Use the properties of a triangle to prove that: **(a)** $|\vec{a} + \vec{b}| \leq |\vec{a}| + |\vec{b}|$; **(b)** $|\vec{a} - \vec{b}| \geq |\vec{a}| - |\vec{b}|$.

7. If $ABCD$ is a quadrilateral where $\overrightarrow{OB} - \overrightarrow{OA} = \overrightarrow{OC} - \overrightarrow{OD}$, prove that $ABCD$ is a parallelogram.

8. If $\vec{a}$, $\vec{b}$, and $\vec{c}$ have a common initial point and are associated with the edges of a parallelepiped, determine vectors representing the diagonals of the parallelepiped.

9. Let $\vec{a}$, $\vec{b}$, and $\vec{c}$ have a common initial point and be associated with the edges of a cube. **(a)** Determine the vectors drawn from the common initial point to each of the other seven vertices. **(b)** Show that the sum of three of these vectors is equal to the sum of the other four.

10. Prove that the sum of the vectors from the center to the vertices of a regular hexagon is a null vector.

1-4 Multiplication of a Vector by a Scalar

Definition 1-6 *Given any real scalar k and any vector $\vec{a}$, the product $k\vec{a}$ is a vector such that $|k\vec{a}| = |k|\,|\vec{a}|$. If $\vec{a}$ is a nonzero vector and k is positive, then $k\vec{a}$ has the same direction as $\vec{a}$; if $\vec{a}$ is a nonzero vector and k is negative, then $k\vec{a}$ has an opposite direction to $\vec{a}$.*

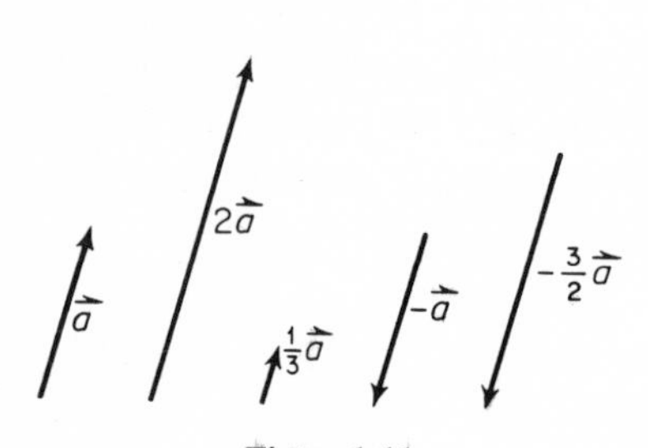

Figure 1-11

In Figure 1-11 several geometric examples of the scalar multiplication of $\vec{a}$ are given. Note that $-\vec{a}$ need not be considered as a special vector, but rather as the product of the scalar -1 and $\vec{a}$. Also note that $\vec{a}$ may be considered as being transformed when multiplied by a scalar k. If $k > 1$, the transformation is a *stretch* or *dilation*; if $0 < k < 1$, the transformation is a *contraction*; if $k < 0$, the transformation is a stretch or a contraction followed by a reversal of direction.

Definition 1-6 for any positive integer k is a logical consequence of a consideration of the way in which the sum of k addends $\vec{a} + \vec{a} + \cdots + \vec{a}$ may be represented.

The multiplication of a vector by a scalar satisfies the distributive and associative laws:

$$(m + n)\vec{a} = m\vec{a} + n\vec{a}, \tag{1-3}$$

$$m(\vec{a} + \vec{b}) = m\vec{a} + m\vec{b}, \tag{1-4}$$

$$m(n\vec{a}) = (mn)\vec{a}. \tag{1-5}$$

The distributive property (1-4) may be illustrated geometrically as in Figure 1-12, using the properties of similar triangles.

If two nonzero vectors $\vec{a}$ and $\vec{b}$ are parallel, then it is possible to find a nonzero scalar m which will transform $\vec{b}$ into $\vec{a}$; that is, $\vec{a} = m\vec{b}$. Similarly, a nonzero scalar n exists which will transform $\vec{a}$ into $\vec{b}$; that is, $\vec{b} = n\vec{a}$. For example, if $\vec{a}$ is a vector parallel to $\vec{b}$ and in the same sense, such that $|\vec{a}| = 2|\vec{b}|$, then $\vec{a} = 2\vec{b}$ and $\vec{b} = \frac{1}{2}\vec{a}$. If $\vec{a}$ is a vector parallel to $\vec{b}$ and in the opposite sense, such that $|\vec{a}| = 2|\vec{b}|$, then $\vec{a} = -2\vec{b}$ and $\vec{b} = -\frac{1}{2}\vec{a}$. Now, considering Definition 1-6 it should be evident that two nonzero vectors are parallel if, and only if, either one may be expressed as a nonzero scalar multiple of the other. We summarize this as a theorem.

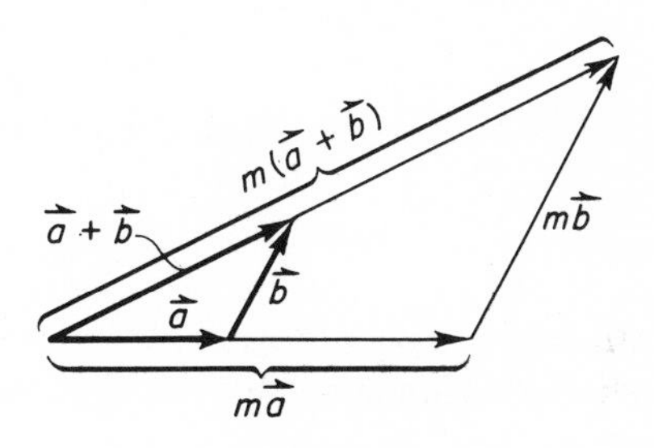

Figure 1-12

Theorem 1-3 *If $\vec{a}$ and $\vec{b}$ are nonzero vectors, then $\vec{a}$ is parallel to $\vec{b}$ if, and only if, there exists a nonzero scalar m or n such that $\vec{a} = m\vec{b}$ or $\vec{b} = n\vec{a}$.*

Since the direction of the null vector is indeterminate, the null vector cannot be parallel to any vector. However, note that the null vector is a zero multiple of every other vector.

Many theorems of plane geometry which involve parallel line segments with related magnitudes may be proved by using Theorem 1-3

Example 1 The line segment joining the mid-points of any two sides of a triangle is parallel to the third side and equal to one-half the length of the third side (Figure 1-13).

Let N and M be the mid-points respectively of sides OB and AB in any triangle OAB. Let $\vec{a}$, $\vec{b}$, and $\vec{c}$ be associated with line segments OA, OB, and NM, respectively. Then

$$\begin{aligned}\overrightarrow{OM} &= \overrightarrow{ON} + \overrightarrow{NM} = \overrightarrow{OA} + \overrightarrow{AM} \\ &= \tfrac{1}{2}\vec{b} + \vec{c} = \vec{a} + \tfrac{1}{2}(\vec{b} - \vec{a}) \\ &= \tfrac{1}{2}\vec{b} + \vec{c} = \tfrac{1}{2}\vec{b} + \tfrac{1}{2}\vec{a}.\end{aligned}$$

Hence $\vec{c} = \frac{1}{2}\vec{a}$; that is, line segment NM is parallel to side OA, and the length of NM is equal to one-half the length of OA.

Example 2 In parallelogram $ABCD$, if M and N are the mid-points of AB and CD, respectively, then $AMCN$ is a parallelogram (Figure 1-14).

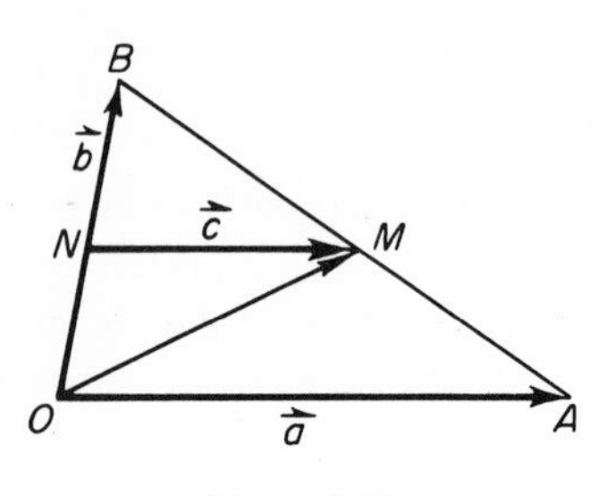

Figure 1-13

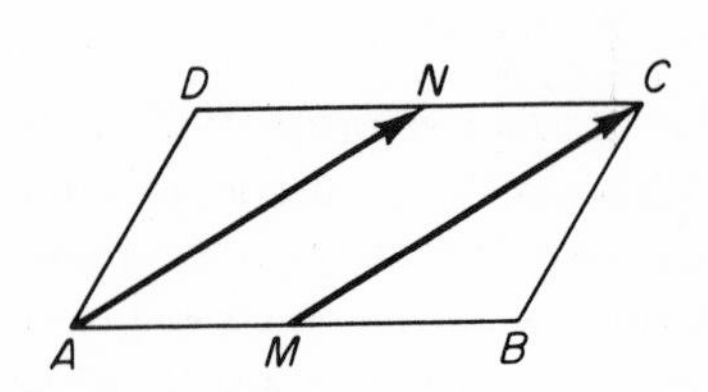

Figure 1-14

Now, $\overrightarrow{AN} = \overrightarrow{AD} + \overrightarrow{DN} = \overrightarrow{AD} + \frac{1}{2}\overrightarrow{DC}$,
and

$$\overrightarrow{MC} = \overrightarrow{MB} + \overrightarrow{BC} = \tfrac{1}{2}\overrightarrow{AB} + \overrightarrow{BC}.$$

Since $\overrightarrow{AB} = \overrightarrow{DC}$ and $\overrightarrow{BC} = \overrightarrow{AD}$, then $\overrightarrow{MC} = \overrightarrow{AN}$. Hence, $AMCN$ is a parallelogram since two opposite sides are equal and parallel.

Example 3 The diagonals of a parallelogram bisect each other (Figure 1-15).

Let $OABC$ be any parallelogram. Let $\vec{a}$ and $\vec{c}$ be associated with sides OA and OC, respectively. Then $\vec{c} - \vec{a}$ and $\vec{c} + \vec{a}$ are the vectors associated with diagonals AC and OB, respectively. If D and E are the mid-points of diagonals OB and AC, respectively, then $\overrightarrow{OD} = \frac{1}{2}(\vec{c} + \vec{a})$, and $\overrightarrow{OE} = \vec{a} + \frac{1}{2}(\vec{c} - \vec{a}) = \frac{1}{2}(\vec{c} + \vec{a})$. Since $\overrightarrow{OD}$ and $\overrightarrow{OE}$ are equal to the same vector, $\overrightarrow{OD} = \overrightarrow{OE}$ and D and E coincide; that is, the diagonals of a parallelogram bisect each other.

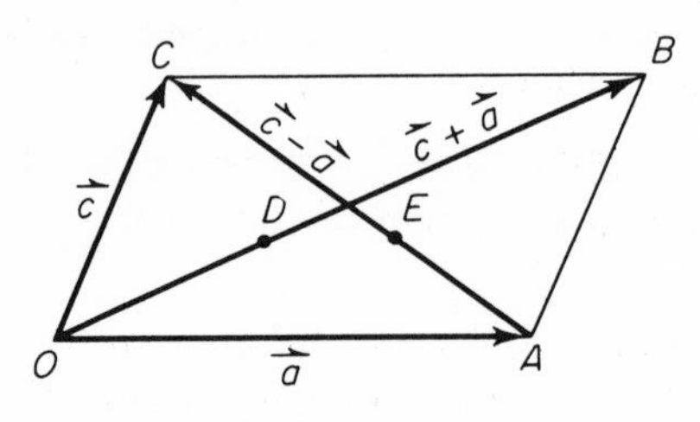

Figure 1-15

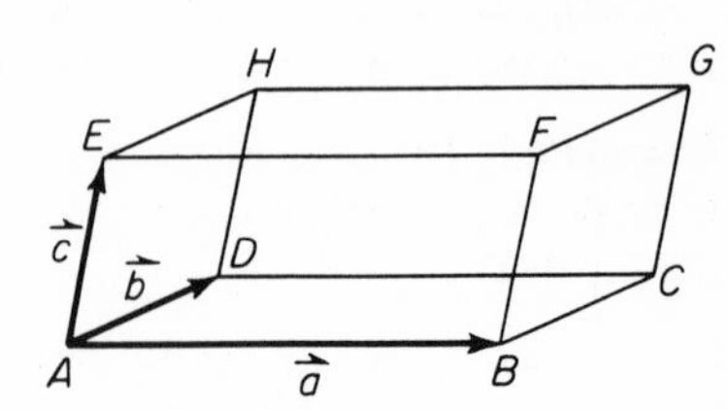

Figure 1-16

Example 4 The diagonals of a parallelepiped bisect each other (Figure 1-16).

Let $\vec{a}$, $\vec{b}$, and $\vec{c}$ be three vectors associated with the edges AB, AD, and AE of any parallelepiped $ABCDEFGH$. Let M, N, R, and S be the mid-points of diagonals AG, EC, BH, and DF, respectively. Then

$$\overrightarrow{AM} = \tfrac{1}{2}\overrightarrow{AG} = \tfrac{1}{2}(\overrightarrow{AB} + \overrightarrow{BC} + \overrightarrow{CG}) = \tfrac{1}{2}(\vec{a} + \vec{b} + \vec{c});$$

$$\overrightarrow{AN} = \tfrac{1}{2}\overrightarrow{AC} + \tfrac{1}{2}\overrightarrow{AE} = \tfrac{1}{2}(\overrightarrow{AB} + \overrightarrow{BC} + \overrightarrow{AE}) = \tfrac{1}{2}(\vec{a} + \vec{b} + \vec{c});$$
$$\overrightarrow{AR} = \tfrac{1}{2}\overrightarrow{AB} + \tfrac{1}{2}\overrightarrow{AH} = \tfrac{1}{2}(\overrightarrow{AB} + \overrightarrow{AD} + \overrightarrow{DH}) = \tfrac{1}{2}(\vec{a} + \vec{b} + \vec{c});$$
$$\overrightarrow{AS} = \tfrac{1}{2}\overrightarrow{AF} + \tfrac{1}{2}\overrightarrow{AD} = \tfrac{1}{2}(\overrightarrow{AB} + \overrightarrow{BF} + \overrightarrow{AD}) = \tfrac{1}{2}(\vec{a} + \vec{b} + \vec{c}).$$

Hence, points M, N, R, and S coincide.

Consider the multiplication of any nonzero vector $\vec{a}$ by a scalar equal to the reciprocal of the magnitude of $\vec{a}$; that is, $(1/|\vec{a}|)\vec{a}$. Let $(1/|\vec{a}|)\vec{a} = \vec{b}$. Then $\vec{a} = |\vec{a}|\,\vec{b}$. By Definition 1-6, $|\vec{a}| = |\vec{a}|\,|\vec{b}|$. Therefore $|\vec{b}| = 1$. Each vector whose magnitude is one is called a **unit vector.** By Theorem 1-3 and Definition 1-6, $\vec{b}$ is parallel to $\vec{a}$ in the same sense. Hence $\vec{b}$, or $(1/|\vec{a}|)\vec{a}$, is a unit vector in the direction $\vec{a}$. We shall make frequent reference to unit vectors in subsequent sections.

Exercises

1. Simplify: **(a)** $\overrightarrow{AB} + \overrightarrow{AB} + \overrightarrow{AB}$; **(b)** $(\overrightarrow{OA} - \overrightarrow{OB}) - (\overrightarrow{OB} - \overrightarrow{OA})$.
2. Select two vectors $\vec{r}$ and $\vec{s}$ of equal magnitude with a common initial point and making an angle of 60°. Then construct the vectors
   (a) $2\vec{r} + \vec{s}$; **(b)** $\vec{r} - 2\vec{s}$; **(c)** $\tfrac{3}{2}\vec{s} - \vec{r}$; **(d)** $2(\vec{r} + \vec{s})$.
3. Illustrate geometrically that $-(\vec{a} - \vec{b}) = -\vec{a} + \vec{b}$.
4. Interpret $\overrightarrow{AB}/|\overrightarrow{AB}|$ for any nonzero vector $\overrightarrow{AB}$.
5. Describe how to construct a parallelogram if two vectors $\vec{a}$ and $\vec{b}$ are given as the diagonals of the parallelogram.

In Exercises 6 through 10 prove the stated theorem.

6. If a line divides two sides of a triangle proportionally, then it is parallel to the third side.
7. The median of a trapezoid is parallel to the bases and equal to one-half their sum.
8. The line segment joining the mid-points of the diagonals of a trapezoid is parallel to the bases and equal to one-half their difference.
9. If M, N, R, and S divide sides AB, BC, CD, and DA of a parallelogram in the same ratio, then $MNRS$ is a parallelogram.
10. If the diagonals of a quadrilateral bisect each other, then the quadrilateral is a parallelogram.

1-5 Linear Dependence of Vectors

In Examples 3 and 4 of §1-4 we considered two geometric problems: one on a plane, and a second in space. In Example 3 we associated two nonzero, nonparallel vectors $\vec{a}$ and $\vec{c}$ with line segments. Then every vector which we considered on the plane was expressed in the form $m\vec{a} + n\vec{c}$; that is, as a function of $\vec{a}$ and $\vec{c}$. Similarly, in Example 4 we associated three nonzero, noncoplanar vectors $\vec{a}$, $\vec{b}$, and $\vec{c}$ with line segments. Then every vector which we considered in space was expressed in the form $m\vec{a} + n\vec{b} + p\vec{c}$; that is, as a function of $\vec{a}$, $\vec{b}$, and $\vec{c}$.

Definition 1-7 *An expression such as* $m_1\overrightarrow{a_1} + m_2\overrightarrow{a_2} + \cdots + m_n\overrightarrow{a_n}$ *which represents the sum of a set of n scalar multiples of n vectors is called a* ***linear function*** *of the n vectors.*

Consider a nonzero vector $\vec{a}$. Then every vector on a line parallel to $\vec{a}$ is a linear function of $\vec{a}$; that is, of the form $m\vec{a}$ where m is a real number. The set of vectors $m\vec{a}$ constitutes a **one-dimensional linear vector space,** and the nonzero vector $\vec{a}$ is called a **basis** for that vector space. Essentially, $\vec{a}$ serves as a reference vector in that every other vector in the one-dimensionals pace may be expressed in terms of $\vec{a}$ or is *dependent* upon $\vec{a}$. Furthermore, any vector of the form $m\vec{a}$ where $m \neq 0$ may be considered a basis of the same one-dimensional linear vector space for which $\vec{a}$ is a basis.

Definition 1-8 *A set of n vectors* $\overrightarrow{a_1}, \overrightarrow{a_2}, \cdots, \overrightarrow{a_n}$ *is called a set of* **linearly independent** *vectors if* $m_1\overrightarrow{a_1} + m_2\overrightarrow{a_2} + \cdots + m_n\overrightarrow{a_n} = \vec{0}$ *implies* $m_1 = m_2 = \cdots = m_n = 0$. *A set of n vectors is called a set of* ***linearly dependent*** *vectors if the vectors are not linearly independent.*

The set of vectors $\vec{a}$ and $\vec{c}$ in Example 3 of §1-4 is a set of linearly independent vectors since $m_1\vec{a} + m_2\vec{c} = \vec{0}$ if, and only if, $m_1 = m_2 = 0$. The set of vectors $\vec{a}$, $\vec{c}$, $\vec{c} + \vec{a}$, and $\vec{c} - \vec{a}$ in that same example is a set of linearly dependent vectors since $m_1\vec{a} + m_2\vec{c} + m_3(\vec{c} + \vec{a}) + m_4(\vec{c} - \vec{a}) = \vec{0}$ is true for $m_1 = m_2 = -1$, $m_3 = 1$, and $m_4 = 0$; that is, for at least one $m_i \neq 0$.

In general, note that by Definition 1-8 n vectors are linearly dependent if at least one of the m_i's in a vector equation of the form $m_1\overrightarrow{a_1} + m_2\overrightarrow{a_2} + \cdots + m_n\overrightarrow{a_n} = \vec{0}$ is not zero. If n vectors are linearly dependent, then at least one of the vectors may be written as a linear function of the other $n - 1$ vectors. For example, if $m_3 \neq 0$, then

$$\overrightarrow{a_3} = -\frac{m_1}{m_3}\overrightarrow{a_1} - \frac{m_2}{m_3}\overrightarrow{a_2} - \frac{m_4}{m_3}\overrightarrow{a_4} - \cdots - \frac{m_n}{m_3}\overrightarrow{a_n}.$$

Conversely, if one vector may be expressed as a linear function of $n - 1$ other vectors, then the n vectors are linearly dependent. It follows from our discussion of a one-dimensional linear vector space that any two vectors in a one-dimensional space are linearly dependent.

Theorem 1-4 *If $\vec{a}$ and $\vec{b}$ are nonzero, nonparallel vectors, then $x\vec{a} + y\vec{b} = \vec{0}$ implies $x = y = 0$.*

Proof: Suppose that $x \neq 0$. Then $x\vec{a} = -y\vec{b}$ and $\vec{a} = -(y/x)\vec{b}$; that is, $\vec{a}$ is parallel to $\vec{b}$ which contradicts the hypothesis. Hence, $x = 0$ and $y\vec{b} = \vec{0}$ implies that $y = 0$ from Definition 1-6.

Any two nonzero, nonparallel vectors $\vec{a}$ and $\vec{b}$ must by Theorem 1-4 be linearly independent. The set of vectors of the form $m\vec{a} + n\vec{b}$, where $\vec{a}$ and $\vec{b}$ are linearly independent vectors and m and n are real scalars, constitutes a **two-dimensional linear vector space.** The two vectors $\vec{a}$ and $\vec{b}$ form a basis for that vector space.

Theorem 1-5 *If $\vec{a}$ and $\vec{b}$ are nonzero, nonparallel vectors with the same initial point, and if $\vec{c}$ is any vector on the plane determined by $\vec{a}$ and $\vec{b}$, then $\vec{c}$ can be expressed as a linear function of $\vec{a}$ and $\vec{b}$.*

Proof: If $\vec{c}$ is parallel to $\vec{a}$, then $\vec{c} = m\vec{a}$; $n = 0$. If $\vec{c}$ is parallel to $\vec{b}$, then $\vec{c} = n\vec{b}$; $m = 0$. If $\vec{c}$ is a null vector, then $m = n = 0$. If $\vec{c}$ is not a null vector and is not parallel to $\vec{a}$ or $\vec{b}$, then there exists a parallelogram $ABCD$ with edges parallel to $\vec{a}$ and $\vec{b}$ and with a diagonal $\vec{c}$. Any vectors parallel to $\vec{a}$ and $\vec{b}$ can be expressed as linear functions of $\vec{a}$ and $\vec{b}$, respectively. Hence $\vec{c} = m\vec{a} + n\vec{b}$ (Figure 1-17).

The converse of Theorem 1-5 is also true; that is, if $\vec{c} = m\vec{a} + n\vec{b}$, where $\vec{a}$ and $\vec{b}$ are nonzero, nonparallel vectors with the same initial point, then $\vec{c}$ may be considered to be on the plane determined by $\vec{a}$ and $\vec{b}$.

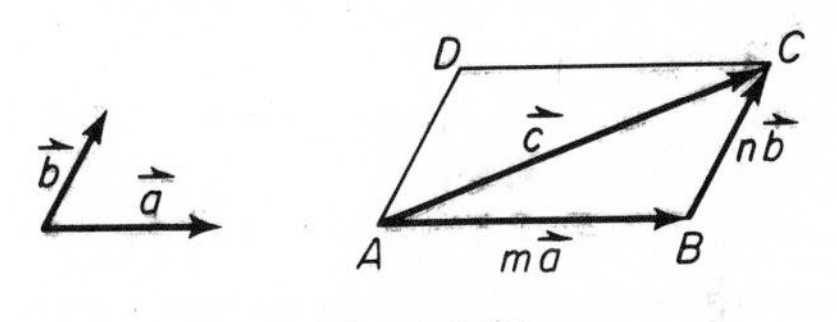

Figure 1-17

Theorem 1-5 implies that any three vectors in a two-dimensional space are linearly dependent.

Theorem 1-6 *If $\vec{a}$, $\vec{b}$, and $\vec{c}$ are nonzero, noncoplanar vectors with the same initial point, then $x\vec{a} + y\vec{b} + z\vec{c} = \vec{0}$ implies $x = y = z = 0$.*

Proof: Suppose that $x \neq 0$. Then $x\vec{a} = -y\vec{b} - z\vec{c}$ and $\vec{a} = -(y/x)\vec{b} - (z/x)\vec{c}$; that is, $\vec{a}$ lies on the plane of $\vec{b}$ and $\vec{c}$ which contradicts the hypothesis that $\vec{a}$, $\vec{b}$, and $\vec{c}$ are noncoplanar. Hence $x = 0$, $y\vec{b} + z\vec{c} = \vec{0}$ and, by Theorem 1-4, $x = y = z = 0$.

Any three nonzero, noncoplanar vectors $\vec{a}$, $\vec{b}$, and $\vec{c}$ with the same initial point must by Theorem 1-6 be linearly independent. The set of vectors of the form $m\vec{a} + n\vec{b} + p\vec{c}$, where $\vec{a}$, $\vec{b}$, and $\vec{c}$ are linearly independent vectors and m, n, and p are real scalars, constitutes a **three-dimensional linear vector space.** The vectors $\vec{a}$, $\vec{b}$, and $\vec{c}$ form a basis for that vector space. We shall refer to a three-dimensional space simply as space.

Theorem 1-7 *If $\vec{a}$, $\vec{b}$, and $\vec{c}$ are nonzero, noncoplanar vectors with the same initial point, then any vector in space can be expressed as a linear function of $\vec{a}$, $\vec{b}$, and $\vec{c}$.*

The proof of Theorem 1-7 is analogous to the proof of Theorem 1-5 and is left as an exercise (Exercise 14). Theorem 1-7 implies that any four vectors in space are linearly dependent.

The concept of a set of linearly independent or dependent vectors plays a key role in proving numerous theorems of geometry by vector methods. Two useful theorems concerning the linear dependence of vectors will now be considered. Careful attention should be paid to these theorems.

Theorem 1-8 *If $\vec{a}$, $\vec{b}$, and $\vec{c}$ are linearly independent vectors, then any vector in space can be expressed as a linear function of $\vec{a}$, $\vec{b}$, and $\vec{c}$ in only one way; that is, every vector in space is a unique linear function of $\vec{a}$, $\vec{b}$, and $\vec{c}$.*

Proof: By Theorem 1-7 every vector $\vec{d}$ in space is a linear function of $\vec{a}$, $\vec{b}$, and $\vec{c}$. Suppose that some vector $\vec{d}$ can be represented in terms of $\vec{a}$, $\vec{b}$, and $\vec{c}$ in two ways; that is,

$$\vec{d} = x\vec{a} + y\vec{b} + z\vec{c} = m\vec{a} + n\vec{b} + p\vec{c}.$$

Then

$$(x - m)\vec{a} + (y - n)\vec{b} + (z - p)\vec{c} = \vec{0}.$$

Since $\vec{a}$, $\vec{b}$, and $\vec{c}$ are linearly independent vectors, then

$$x - m = 0; \qquad y - n = 0; \qquad z - p = 0.$$

Hence $x = m$; $y = n$; $z = p$; and the two representations of $\vec{d}$ are identical.

In any geometry of n dimensions, Theorem 1-8 may be generalized for a set of n linearly independent vectors $\overrightarrow{a_1}, \overrightarrow{a_2}, \cdots, \overrightarrow{a_n}$. Any vector which is a linear function of $\overrightarrow{a_1}, \overrightarrow{a_2}, \cdots, \overrightarrow{a_n}$ can be expressed as a linear function of the n vectors in only one way. The proof of the generalized theorem is left as an exercise (Exercise 15).

Theorem 1-9 *The points A, B, and C are collinear if, and only if, for any point O in space $\overrightarrow{OC} = (1 - n)\,\overrightarrow{OA} + n\overrightarrow{OB}$.*

Proof: Let O be any reference point in space and C be any point on the line AB. Then $\overrightarrow{OC}$ is a vector whose terminal point C lies on the line through the terminal points A and B of $\overrightarrow{OA}$ and $\overrightarrow{OB}$. Furthermore, consider C dividing line segment BA in the ratio m to n where $m + n = 1$ (Figure 1-18). Now,

$$\overrightarrow{OC} = \overrightarrow{OA} + \overrightarrow{AC} = \overrightarrow{OA} + n\overrightarrow{AB}$$
$$= \overrightarrow{OA} + n(\overrightarrow{OB} - \overrightarrow{OA})$$
$$= (1 - n)\overrightarrow{OA} + n\overrightarrow{OB}.$$

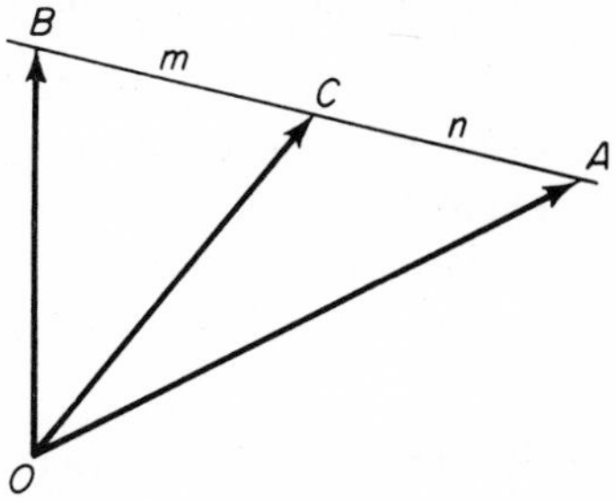

Figure 1-18

Conversely, if $\overrightarrow{OC} = (1 - n)\overrightarrow{OA} + n\overrightarrow{OB}$, then

$$\overrightarrow{OC} = \overrightarrow{OA} - n\overrightarrow{OA} + n\overrightarrow{OB}$$
$$\overrightarrow{OC} - \overrightarrow{OA} = n(\overrightarrow{OB} - \overrightarrow{OA})$$
$$\overrightarrow{AC} = n\overrightarrow{AB}.$$

Therefore, $\overrightarrow{AC}$ is parallel to $\overrightarrow{AB}$; line segment AC lies along line segment AB; and A, B, and C are collinear.

Exercises

In Exercises 1 through 8 consider the vectors given in the figure and express each vector as a linear function of (**a**) $\overrightarrow{OA}$ *and* $\overrightarrow{OB}$; (**b**) $\overrightarrow{OB}$ *and* $\overrightarrow{OC}$; (**c**) $\overrightarrow{OA}$ *and* $\overrightarrow{OD}$.

1. $\overrightarrow{OA}$. **2.** $\overrightarrow{OB}$.

3. $\overrightarrow{OC}$. **4.** $\overrightarrow{OD}$.

5. $\overrightarrow{OE}$. **6.** $\overrightarrow{CA}$.

7. $\overrightarrow{AB}$. **8.** $\overrightarrow{ED}$.

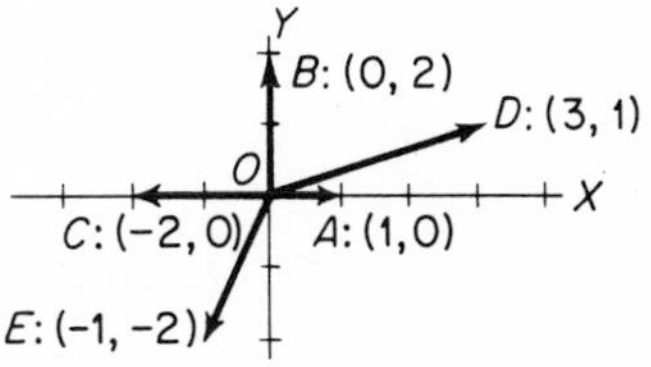

9. Prove that M is the mid-point of line segment AB if $\overrightarrow{OM} + \overrightarrow{OM} = \overrightarrow{OA} + \overrightarrow{OB}$.

10. Prove that $4\overrightarrow{MN} = \overrightarrow{AB} + \overrightarrow{AD} + \overrightarrow{CB} + \overrightarrow{CD}$ if M and N are the mid-points of line segments AC and BD, respectively.

11. Prove that the terminal points of vectors $\overrightarrow{AB}$, $\overrightarrow{AC}$, and $\overrightarrow{AD}$ are collinear if $\overrightarrow{AD} = \overrightarrow{AB} + \frac{2}{5}(\overrightarrow{OC} - \overrightarrow{OB})$.

12. Prove that the vectors $\vec{a} + 2\vec{b} + \vec{c}$, $\vec{a} + 3\vec{b} - 2\vec{c}$, $\vec{a} + \vec{b} + 4\vec{c}$ are linearly dependent.

13. Find another set of vectors which may be a basis for the two-dimensional linear vector space for which the set $\vec{a}$ and $\vec{b}$ is a basis.

14. Prove Theorem 1-7.

15. Prove that any vector which is a linear function of n linearly independent vectors $\vec{a}_1, \vec{a}_2, \cdots, \vec{a}_n$ is a unique linear function of the n vectors.

16. Prove that a necessary and sufficient condition for the terminal points of any three nonzero vectors $\vec{a}$, $\vec{b}$, and $\vec{c}$ with common initial point to be collinear is the implication of the equation $x\vec{a} + y\vec{b} + z\vec{c} = \vec{0}$ that $x + y + z = 0$, provided $x^2 + y^2 + z^2 \neq 0$.

1-6 Applications of Linear Dependence

In this section several theorems of plane synthetic geometry will be proved by using the concept of linear dependence of a set of vectors. Most vector proofs involving the linear dependence concept depend upon Theorems 1-8 and 1-9.

Example 1 The line segment joining a vertex of a parallelogram to the mid-point of a nonadjacent side intersects the diagonal at a trisection point (Figure 1-19).

Let $ABCD$ be any parallelogram. Let M be the mid-point of side BC and P be the point of intersection of line segment AM and diagonal BD. Now,

$$\begin{aligned}\overrightarrow{AM} &= \tfrac{1}{2}\overrightarrow{AB} + \tfrac{1}{2}\overrightarrow{AC} = \tfrac{1}{2}\overrightarrow{AB} + \tfrac{1}{2}(\overrightarrow{AD} + \overrightarrow{DC}) = \tfrac{1}{2}\overrightarrow{AB} + \tfrac{1}{2}(\overrightarrow{AD} + \overrightarrow{AB})\\ &= \overrightarrow{AB} + \tfrac{1}{2}\overrightarrow{AD},\end{aligned}$$

and

$$\overrightarrow{AP} = k\overrightarrow{AM} = k\overrightarrow{AB} + \frac{k}{2}\overrightarrow{AD}.$$

Since B, P, and D are collinear, $k + k/2 = 1$ or $k = \frac{2}{3}$. Hence, $\overrightarrow{AP} = \frac{2}{3}\overrightarrow{AB} + \frac{1}{3}\overrightarrow{AD}$; that is, P divides diagonal BD in the ratio 1 to 2.

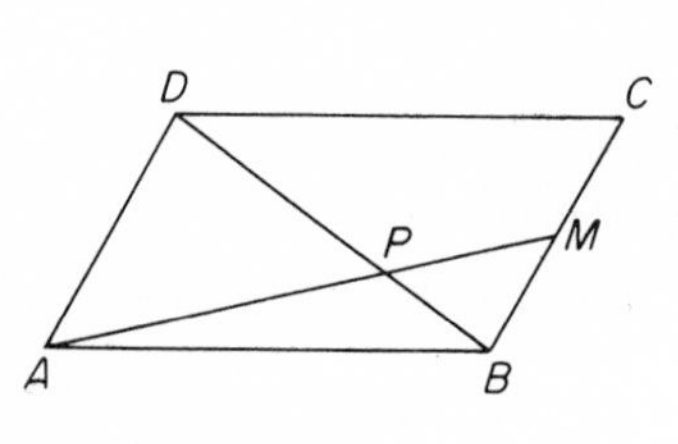

Figure 1-19

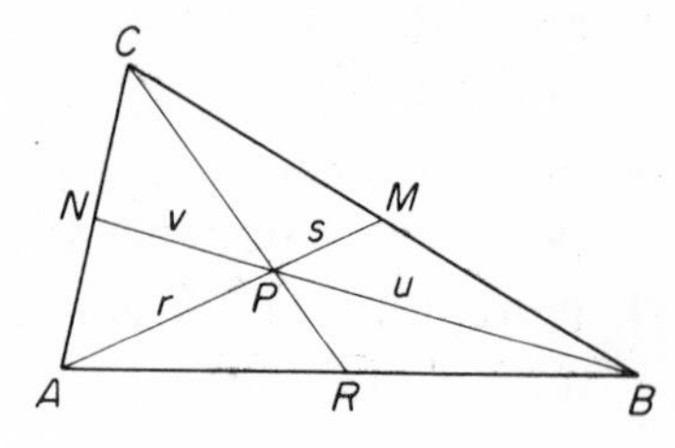

Figure 1-20

Example 2 The medians of a triangle are concurrent at a point called the **centroid** of the triangle. This point is two-thirds of the distance from each vertex to the mid-point of the opposite side (Figure 1-20).

Let M, N, and R be the mid-points of sides BC, CA, and AB, respectively, of any triangle ABC. Let P be the point of intersection of the medians AM and BN. Consider P dividing median AM in the ratio r to s where $r + s = 1$ and dividing median BN in the ratio u to v where $u + v = 1$. Let O be any reference point in space not in the plane of triangle ABC. Now,

$$\overrightarrow{OP} = r\overrightarrow{OM} + s\overrightarrow{OA} = u\overrightarrow{ON} + v\overrightarrow{OB}.$$

Since M and N are mid-points of sides BC and CA, respectively,

$$\overrightarrow{OM} = \tfrac{1}{2}\overrightarrow{OB} + \tfrac{1}{2}\overrightarrow{OC}, \quad \text{and} \quad \overrightarrow{ON} = \tfrac{1}{2}\overrightarrow{OA} + \tfrac{1}{2}\overrightarrow{OC}.$$

By substitution,

$$\overrightarrow{OP} = \frac{r}{2}(\overrightarrow{OB} + \overrightarrow{OC}) + s\overrightarrow{OA} = \frac{u}{2}(\overrightarrow{OA} + \overrightarrow{OC}) + v\overrightarrow{OB}.$$

Since $\overrightarrow{OA}$, $\overrightarrow{OB}$, and $\overrightarrow{OC}$ are linearly independent vectors,

$$s = \frac{u}{2}; \quad \frac{r}{2} = v; \quad \frac{r}{2} = \frac{u}{2}.$$

Therefore, $r = 2s$ and $u = 2v$. Hence, P divides both medians AM and BN in the ratio 2 to 1. Consider the medians CR and AM. Since their point of intersection must divide medians AM and CR in the ratio 2 to 1 by the same argument, median CR passes through P.

Example 3 In any quadrilateral the line segments joining the mid-points of opposite sides bisect each other (Figure 1-21).

Let M, N, R, and S be the mid-points of sides AB, BC, CD, and DA, respectively, of any quadrilateral. Let P and P' be the mid-points of line segments MR and NS, respectively. If O is any reference point, then

$$\overrightarrow{OP} = \tfrac{1}{2}\overrightarrow{OM} + \tfrac{1}{2}\overrightarrow{OR} = \tfrac{1}{4}(\overrightarrow{OA} + \overrightarrow{OB} + \overrightarrow{OC} + \overrightarrow{OD});$$

$$\overrightarrow{OP'} = \tfrac{1}{2}\overrightarrow{ON} + \tfrac{1}{2}\overrightarrow{OS} = \tfrac{1}{4}(\overrightarrow{OB} + \overrightarrow{OC} + \overrightarrow{OA} + \overrightarrow{OD}).$$

Since $\overrightarrow{OP} = \overrightarrow{OP'}$, the points P and P' coincide.

A study of the properties and relations among the internal and external bisectors of the angles of a triangle may be facilitated by the use of vectors. The vector form of the bisector of an angle may be found as follows: Consider $\vec{a}$ and $\vec{b}$ as unit vectors along lines OA' and OB', respectively (Figure 1-22). Construct a rhombus $OACB$ by finding point C which is one unit from points A and B and draw the diagonal OC. Now ray OC bisects angle AOB, since the diagonal of a rhombus bisects its angles. Any multiple of $\overrightarrow{OC}$ lies along the angle bisector of angle AOB. Since $\overrightarrow{OC} = \vec{a} + \vec{b}$, then $k(\vec{a} + \vec{b})$, where k is any non-negative real number, represents the vector form of the bisector of an angle between the unit vectors $\vec{a}$ and $\vec{b}$.

The bisector of the supplementary angle of the angle between $\vec{a}$ and $\vec{b}$

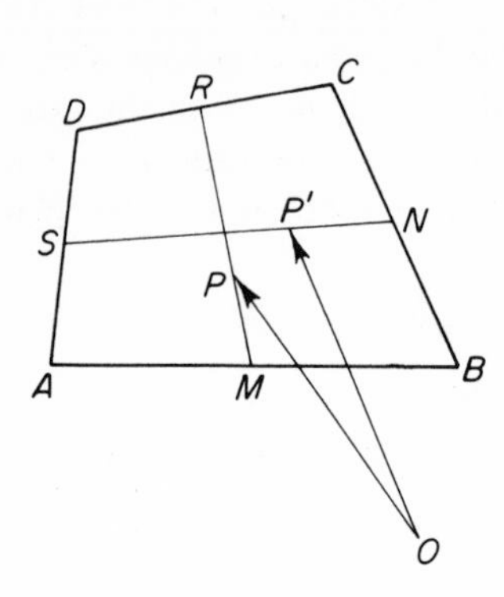

Figure 1-21

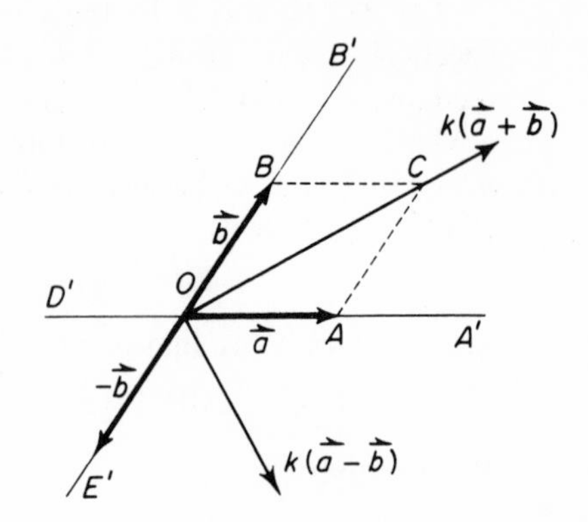

Figure 1-22

may be expressed in vector form as $k(\vec{a} - \vec{b})$. If k is non-negative, $k(\vec{a} - b)$ represents the bisector of angle $A'OE'$. If k is negative or zero, $k(\vec{a} - \vec{b})$ represents the bisector of angle $B'OD'$.

Example 4 The angle bisector of an interior angle of a triangle divides the opposite side into segments which are proportional to the adjacent sides (Figure 1-23).

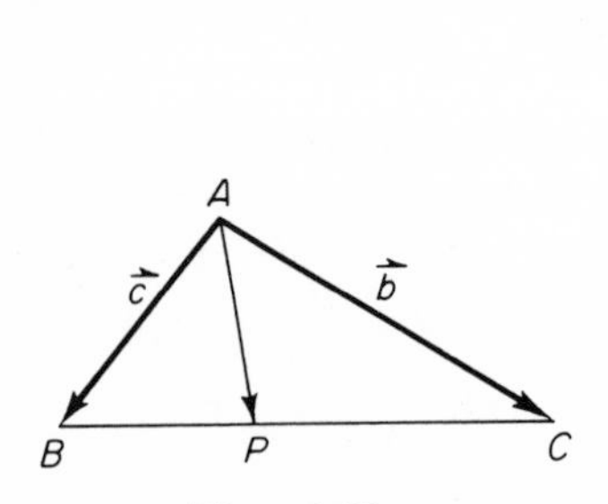

Figure 1-23

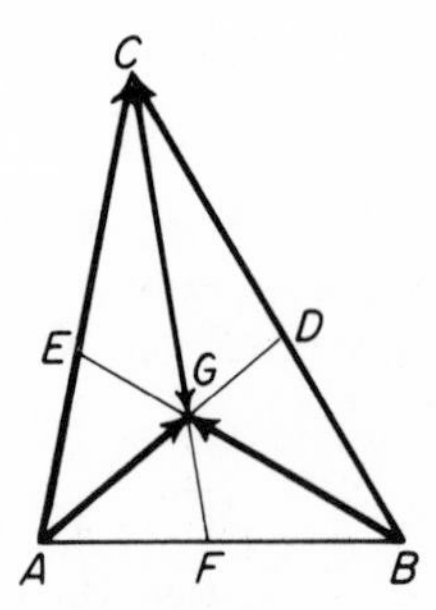

Figure 1-24

Associate vectors $\vec{b}$ and $\vec{c}$ with sides AC and AB, respectively, of any triangle ABC. Let ray AP be the internal bisector of angle A where P lies on line segment BC. Then

$$\overrightarrow{AP} = k\left(\frac{\vec{b}}{|\vec{b}|} + \frac{\vec{c}}{|\vec{c}|}\right) = k\left(\frac{|\vec{c}|\,\vec{b} + |\vec{b}|\,\vec{c}}{|\vec{b}|\,|\vec{c}|}\right)$$

where, by Theorem 1-9, k is such that the sum of the coefficients of $\vec{b}$ and $\vec{c}$ is one. Then

$$k = \frac{|\vec{b}||\vec{c}|}{|\vec{b}| + |\vec{c}|}, \quad \text{and} \quad \overrightarrow{AP} = \frac{|\vec{c}|}{|\vec{b}| + |\vec{c}|}\vec{b} + \frac{|\vec{b}|}{|\vec{b}| + |\vec{c}|}\vec{c}.$$

Hence,

$$\frac{|\overrightarrow{BP}|}{|\overrightarrow{PC}|} = \frac{\dfrac{|\vec{c}|}{|\vec{b}| + |\vec{c}|}}{\dfrac{|\vec{b}|}{|\vec{b}| + |\vec{c}|}} = \frac{|\vec{c}|}{|\vec{b}|} = \frac{|\overrightarrow{AB}|}{|\overrightarrow{AC}|}.$$

Example 5 The angle bisectors of the interior angles of a triangle are concurrent (Figure 1-24).

Let ABC be any triangle with rays AD and BE, the internal bisectors of angles A and B, respectively. Let rays AD and BE intersect at point G. Now,

$$\overrightarrow{AG} = x\left(\frac{\overrightarrow{AB}}{|\overrightarrow{AB}|} + \frac{\overrightarrow{AC}}{|\overrightarrow{AC}|}\right) \quad \text{and} \quad \overrightarrow{BG} = y\left(-\frac{\overrightarrow{AB}}{|\overrightarrow{AB}|} + \frac{\overrightarrow{BC}}{|\overrightarrow{BC}|}\right).$$

Then,

$$\begin{aligned}\overrightarrow{CG} = \overrightarrow{AG} - \overrightarrow{AC} &= x\left(\frac{\overrightarrow{AB}}{|\overrightarrow{AB}|} + \frac{\overrightarrow{AC}}{|\overrightarrow{AC}|}\right) - \overrightarrow{AC} \\ &= x\frac{\overrightarrow{AB}}{|\overrightarrow{AB}|} + (x - |\overrightarrow{AC}|)\frac{\overrightarrow{AC}}{|\overrightarrow{AC}|},\end{aligned}$$

and

$$\begin{aligned}\overrightarrow{CG} = \overrightarrow{BG} - \overrightarrow{BC} &= y\left(-\frac{\overrightarrow{AB}}{|\overrightarrow{AB}|} + \frac{\overrightarrow{AC} - \overrightarrow{AB}}{|\overrightarrow{BC}|}\right) - \overrightarrow{AC} + \overrightarrow{AB} \\ &= \left(-y - \frac{|\overrightarrow{AB}|}{|\overrightarrow{BC}|}y + |\overrightarrow{AB}|\right)\frac{\overrightarrow{AB}}{|\overrightarrow{AB}|} \\ &\quad + \left(\frac{|\overrightarrow{AC}|}{|\overrightarrow{BC}|}y - |\overrightarrow{AC}|\right)\frac{\overrightarrow{AC}}{|\overrightarrow{AC}|}.\end{aligned}$$

Since $\overrightarrow{AB}/|\overrightarrow{AB}|$ and $\overrightarrow{AC}/|\overrightarrow{AC}|$ are linearly independent vectors,

$$x = -y - \frac{|\overrightarrow{AB}|}{|\overrightarrow{BC}|}y + |\overrightarrow{AB}|$$

and

$$x - |\overrightarrow{AC}| = \frac{|\overrightarrow{AC}|}{|\overrightarrow{BC}|}y - |\overrightarrow{AC}|.$$

Therefore

$$x = \frac{|\overrightarrow{AC}|}{|\overrightarrow{BC}|}y, \qquad y\left(1 + \frac{|\overrightarrow{AB}|}{|\overrightarrow{BC}|} + \frac{|\overrightarrow{AC}|}{|\overrightarrow{BC}|}\right) = |\overrightarrow{AB}|;$$

$$y = \frac{|\overrightarrow{AB}|\,|\overrightarrow{BC}|}{|\overrightarrow{AB}| + |\overrightarrow{BC}| + |\overrightarrow{AC}|};$$

$$x = \frac{|\overrightarrow{AB}|\,|\overrightarrow{AC}|}{|\overrightarrow{AB}| + |\overrightarrow{AC}| + |\overrightarrow{BC}|}.$$

Then

$$\begin{aligned}
\overrightarrow{CG} &= \frac{|\overrightarrow{AB}|\,|\overrightarrow{AC}|}{|\overrightarrow{AB}| + |\overrightarrow{AC}| + |\overrightarrow{BC}|}\left(\frac{\overrightarrow{AB}}{|\overrightarrow{AB}|} + \frac{\overrightarrow{AC}}{|\overrightarrow{AC}|}\right) - \overrightarrow{AC} \\
&= \frac{|\overrightarrow{AB}|\,|\overrightarrow{AC}|}{|\overrightarrow{AB}| + |\overrightarrow{AC}| + |\overrightarrow{BC}|}\left(\frac{\overrightarrow{CB} - \overrightarrow{CA}}{|\overrightarrow{AB}|} - \frac{\overrightarrow{CA}}{|\overrightarrow{AC}|}\right) + \overrightarrow{CA} \\
&= \frac{1}{|\overrightarrow{AB}| + |\overrightarrow{AC}| + |\overrightarrow{BC}|}[|\overrightarrow{AC}|\,\overrightarrow{CB} - |\overrightarrow{AC}|\,\overrightarrow{CA} - |\overrightarrow{AB}|\,\overrightarrow{CA} \\
&\quad + (|\overrightarrow{AB}| + |\overrightarrow{AC}| + |\overrightarrow{BC}|)\overrightarrow{CA}] \\
&= \frac{|\overrightarrow{BC}|}{|\overrightarrow{AB}| + |\overrightarrow{AC}| + |\overrightarrow{BC}|}\overrightarrow{CA} + \frac{|\overrightarrow{AC}|}{|\overrightarrow{AB}| + |\overrightarrow{AC}| + |\overrightarrow{BC}|}\overrightarrow{CB} \\
&= \frac{|\overrightarrow{AC}|\,|\overrightarrow{BC}|}{|\overrightarrow{AB}| + |\overrightarrow{AC}| + |\overrightarrow{BC}|}\left(\frac{\overrightarrow{CA}}{|\overrightarrow{CA}|} + \frac{\overrightarrow{CB}}{|\overrightarrow{CB}|}\right).
\end{aligned}$$

Hence, ray CG is the angle bisector of angle C.

Example 6 The two lines determined by the external bisectors of two angles of a triangle and the internal bisector of the third angle are concurrent (Figure 1-25).

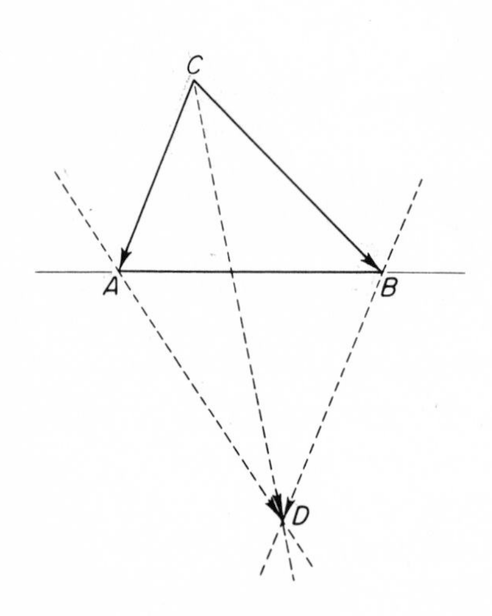

Figure 1-25

Let ABC be any triangle with lines AD and BD determined by the external bisectors of angles A and B, respectively. By the discussion preceding Example 4,

$$\overrightarrow{AD} = x\left(\frac{\overrightarrow{AB}}{|\overrightarrow{AB}|} + \frac{\overrightarrow{CA}}{|\overrightarrow{CA}|}\right)$$

and

$$\overrightarrow{BD} = y\left(-\frac{\overrightarrow{AB}}{|\overrightarrow{AB}|} + \frac{\overrightarrow{CB}}{|\overrightarrow{CB}|}\right).$$

Now,

$$\begin{aligned}\overrightarrow{CD} &= \overrightarrow{CA} + \overrightarrow{AD}\\ &= \overrightarrow{CA} + x\left(\frac{\overrightarrow{CB}-\overrightarrow{CA}}{|\overrightarrow{AB}|} + \frac{\overrightarrow{CA}}{|\overrightarrow{CA}|}\right)\\ &= \left(|\overrightarrow{CA}| - \frac{|\overrightarrow{CA}|}{|\overrightarrow{AB}|}x + x\right)\frac{\overrightarrow{CA}}{|\overrightarrow{CA}|} + \left(\frac{|\overrightarrow{CB}|}{|\overrightarrow{AB}|}x\right)\frac{\overrightarrow{CB}}{|\overrightarrow{CB}|};\\ \overrightarrow{CD} &= \overrightarrow{CB} + \overrightarrow{BD}\\ &= \overrightarrow{CB} + y\left(-\frac{\overrightarrow{CB}-\overrightarrow{CA}}{|\overrightarrow{AB}|} + \frac{\overrightarrow{CB}}{|\overrightarrow{CB}|}\right)\\ &= \left(\frac{|\overrightarrow{CA}|}{|\overrightarrow{AB}|}y\right)\frac{\overrightarrow{CA}}{|\overrightarrow{CA}|} + \left(|\overrightarrow{CB}| - \frac{|\overrightarrow{CB}|}{|\overrightarrow{AB}|}y + y\right)\frac{\overrightarrow{CB}}{|\overrightarrow{CB}|}.\end{aligned}$$

Since $\overrightarrow{CA}/|\overrightarrow{CA}|$ and $\overrightarrow{CB}/|\overrightarrow{CB}|$ are linearly independent vectors,

$$\frac{|\overrightarrow{CB}|}{|\overrightarrow{AB}|}x = |\overrightarrow{CB}| - \frac{|\overrightarrow{CB}|}{|\overrightarrow{AB}|}y + y,$$

and

$$|\overrightarrow{CA}| - \frac{|\overrightarrow{CA}|}{|\overrightarrow{AB}|}x + x = \frac{|\overrightarrow{CA}|}{|\overrightarrow{AB}|}y.$$

Then

$$x = |\overrightarrow{AB}| - y + \frac{|\overrightarrow{AB}|}{|\overrightarrow{CB}|}y = \frac{|\overrightarrow{AB}|\,|\overrightarrow{CA}|}{|\overrightarrow{CA}| + |\overrightarrow{CB}| - |\overrightarrow{AB}|}.$$

Then

$$\begin{aligned}\overrightarrow{CD} &= \overrightarrow{CA} + \frac{|\overrightarrow{AB}|\,|\overrightarrow{CA}|}{|\overrightarrow{CA}| + |\overrightarrow{CB}| - |\overrightarrow{AB}|}\left(\frac{\overrightarrow{CB}-\overrightarrow{CA}}{|\overrightarrow{AB}|} + \frac{\overrightarrow{CA}}{|\overrightarrow{CA}|}\right)\\ &= \frac{|\overrightarrow{CB}|}{|\overrightarrow{CA}| + |\overrightarrow{CB}| - |\overrightarrow{AB}|}\overrightarrow{CA} + \frac{|\overrightarrow{CA}|}{|\overrightarrow{CA}| + |\overrightarrow{CB}| - |\overrightarrow{AB}|}\overrightarrow{CB}\\ &= \frac{|\overrightarrow{CA}|\,|\overrightarrow{CB}|}{|\overrightarrow{CA}| + |\overrightarrow{CB}| - |\overrightarrow{AB}|}\left(\frac{\overrightarrow{CA}}{|\overrightarrow{CA}|} + \frac{\overrightarrow{CB}}{|\overrightarrow{CB}|}\right).\end{aligned}$$

Hence, line CD is determined by the internal bisector of angle C.

The remaining examples of this section illustrate the use of the concept of linear dependence of vectors in proving two important theorems of higher geometry.

Example 7—*Theorem of Menelaus* Given triangle ABC, three distinct points P_1, P_2, and P_3 on lines along sides AB, BC, and CA, respectively, are collinear if, and only if,

$$\left(\frac{\overrightarrow{AP_1}}{\overrightarrow{P_1B}}\right)\left(\frac{\overrightarrow{BP_2}}{\overrightarrow{P_2C}}\right)\left(\frac{\overrightarrow{CP_3}}{\overrightarrow{P_3A}}\right) = -1$$

where each quotient represents the real number that may be obtained when the two collinear vectors are expressed as multiples of the same vector (Figure 1-26).

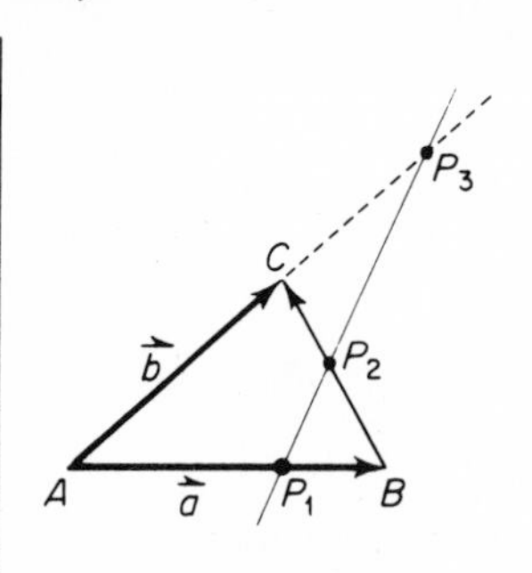

Figure 1-26

Let $\overrightarrow{AB} = \vec{a}$ and $\overrightarrow{AC} = \vec{b}$. Then $\overrightarrow{BC} = \vec{b} - \vec{a}$. Let $\overrightarrow{AP_1} = n\vec{a}$, $\overrightarrow{P_1B} = (1 - n)\vec{a}$, $\overrightarrow{BP_2} = k(\vec{b} - \vec{a})$, $\overrightarrow{P_2C} = (1 - k)(\vec{b} - \vec{a})$, $\overrightarrow{CP_3} = (m - 1)\vec{b}$, and $\overrightarrow{P_3A} = -m\vec{b}$.

We first prove the necessary condition for P_1, P_2, and P_3 to be collinear.

If P_1, P_2, and P_3 are collinear, then

$$\begin{aligned}\overrightarrow{AP_2} &= t\overrightarrow{AP_1} + (1 - t)\overrightarrow{AP_3}\\ &= tn\vec{a} + (1 - t)m\vec{b}.\end{aligned}$$

Since $\overrightarrow{AP_2} = (1 - k)\vec{a} + k\vec{b}$, and $\vec{a}$ and $\vec{b}$ are linearly independent vectors, then $tn = 1 - k$ and $(1 - t)m = k$; that is,

$$n = \frac{1 - k}{t}, \qquad \text{and} \qquad m = \frac{k}{1 - t}.$$

Therefore,

$$\begin{aligned}\frac{\overrightarrow{AP_1}}{\overrightarrow{P_1B}} \cdot \frac{\overrightarrow{BP_2}}{\overrightarrow{P_2C}} \cdot \frac{\overrightarrow{CP_3}}{\overrightarrow{P_3A}} &= \frac{n\vec{a}}{(1 - n)\vec{a}} \cdot \frac{k(\vec{b} - \vec{a})}{(1 - k)(\vec{b} - \vec{a})} \cdot \frac{(m - 1)\vec{b}}{-m\vec{b}}\\ &= \frac{n}{1 - n} \cdot \frac{k}{1 - k} \cdot \frac{m - 1}{-m}\\ &= \frac{1 - k}{t - 1 + k} \cdot \frac{k}{1 - k} \cdot \frac{k - 1 + t}{-k} = -1.\end{aligned}$$

Next we assume that P_1, P_2, and P_3 divide sides AB, BC, and CA in the ratios $n/(1 - n)$, $k/(1 - k)$, and $(1 - n)(k - 1)/nk$, respectively; that is, the product of the ratios is -1. Let O be any point in the plane of triangle ABC. Then

$$\overrightarrow{OP_1} = n\overrightarrow{OB} + (1 - n)\overrightarrow{OA};\ \overrightarrow{OP_2} = k\overrightarrow{OC} + (1 - k)\overrightarrow{OB};$$

and since $(1 - n)(k - 1) + nk = n + k - 1$,

$$\overrightarrow{OP_3} = \frac{(1 - n)(k - 1)}{n + k - 1}\overrightarrow{OA} + \frac{nk}{n + k - 1}\overrightarrow{OC}.$$

Substituting for $(1 - n)\overrightarrow{OA}$ and $k\overrightarrow{OC}$,

$$\begin{aligned}\overrightarrow{OP_3} &= \frac{k - 1}{n + k - 1}(\overrightarrow{OP_1} - n\overrightarrow{OB}) + \frac{n}{n + k - 1}[\overrightarrow{OP_2} - (1 - k)\overrightarrow{OB}]\\ &= \frac{k - 1}{n + k - 1}\overrightarrow{OP_1} + \frac{n}{n + k - 1}\overrightarrow{OP_2}.\end{aligned}$$

Since

$$\frac{k-1}{n+k-1} + \frac{n}{n+k-1} = 1,$$

P_1, P_2, and P_3 are collinear (Theorem 1-9).

Example 8—*Desargues' Theorem* If two triangles ABC and $A'B'C'$ are such that lines joining corresponding vertices are concurrent and no two corresponding sides are parallel, then the lines determined by the corresponding sides intersect in three collinear points.

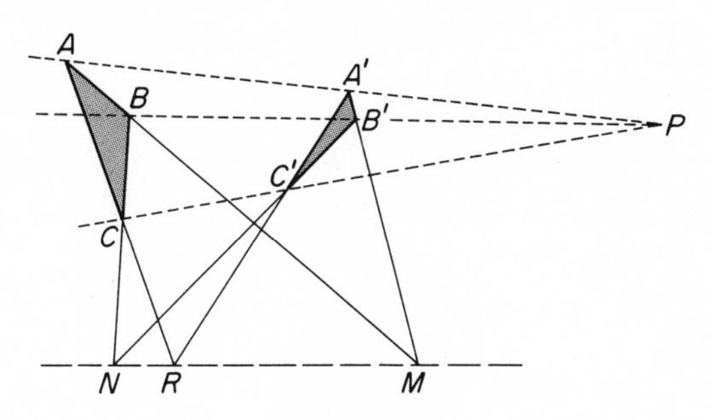

Figure 1-27

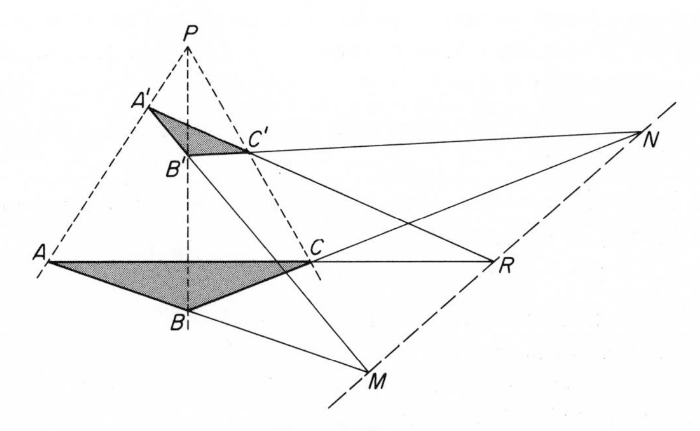

Figure 1-28

Figure 1-27 represents Desargues' configuration for coplanar triangles, and Figure 1-28 represents Desargues' configuration for triangles that are not coplanar.

Let O be any reference point in space. Now,

$$\overrightarrow{OP} = x\overrightarrow{OA} + (1-x)\overrightarrow{OA'} = y\overrightarrow{OB} + (1-y)\overrightarrow{OB'}$$
$$= z\overrightarrow{OC} + (1-z)\overrightarrow{OC'}.$$

Then $x \neq y$ since line AB is not parallel to line $A'B'$. Therefore,

$$\frac{x\overrightarrow{OA} - y\overrightarrow{OB}}{x - y} = \frac{(1 - y)\overrightarrow{OB'} - (1 - x)\overrightarrow{OA'}}{x - y};$$

that is, there exists a point common to lines AB and $A'B'$. Call the point M. Similarly, $y \neq z$, $x \neq z$, and points N and R exist common to the lines BC and $B'C'$ and the lines AC and $A'C'$, respectively, since

$$\frac{y\overrightarrow{OB} - z\overrightarrow{OC}}{y - z} = \frac{(1 - z)\overrightarrow{OC'} - (1 - y)\overrightarrow{OB'}}{y - z}$$

and

$$\frac{z\overrightarrow{OC} - x\overrightarrow{OA}}{z - x} = \frac{(1 - x)\overrightarrow{OA'} - (1 - z)\overrightarrow{OC'}}{z - x}.$$

Now

$$\begin{aligned}(x - y)\overrightarrow{OM} + (y - z)\overrightarrow{ON} + (z - x)\overrightarrow{OR} \\ = x\overrightarrow{OA} - y\overrightarrow{OB} + y\overrightarrow{OB} - z\overrightarrow{OC} + z\overrightarrow{OC} - x\overrightarrow{OA} = \vec{0},\end{aligned}$$

and the sum of the multiples of $\overrightarrow{OM}$, $\overrightarrow{ON}$, and $\overrightarrow{OR}$ is zero. Hence M, N, and R are collinear.

Exercises

Use the concept of linear dependence of vectors to prove the theorems stated in Exercises 1 through 14.

1. A line segment joining a vertex of a parallelogram to a point which divides an opposite side in the ratio 1 to n divides the diagonal in the ratio 1 to $n + 1$ or n to $n + 1$.
2. The sum of the vectors associated with the medians of a triangle is equal to the null vector.
3. A vector $\overrightarrow{OP}$ from any reference point O to the centroid P of any triangle ABC may be expressed by
$$\overrightarrow{OP} = \tfrac{1}{3}(\overrightarrow{OA} + \overrightarrow{OB} + \overrightarrow{OC}).$$
4. If line segments from two vertices of a triangle trisect the opposite sides as shown in the figure, then the point P divides both line segments AM and BN in the ratio 3 to 2.

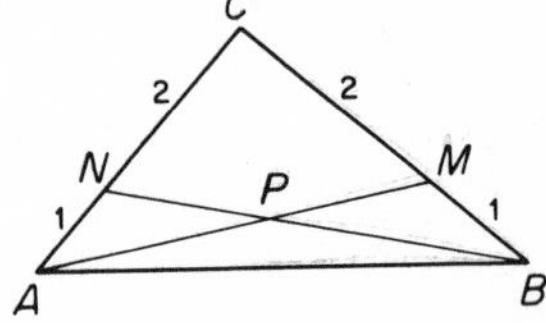

5. The line segments joining the mid-points of the adjacent sides of any quadrilateral form a parallelogram.
6. Let $ABCD$ be any quadrilateral. If O is any reference point, then $\overrightarrow{OP} = \tfrac{1}{4}(\overrightarrow{OA} + \overrightarrow{OB} + \overrightarrow{OC} + \overrightarrow{OD})$ where P is the mid-point of the line segment joining the mid-points of diagonals AC and BD.
7. The line segments joining the mid-points of the opposite edges of a tetrahedron bisect each other.

8. If a parallelogram is defined as a quadrilateral whose opposite sides are parallel, then the opposite sides of a parallelogram are equal.
9. The sum of the vectors from the center to the vertices of a regular pentagon is a null vector.
10. The lines determined by the external bisectors of the angles of a triangle intersect respectively the lines determined by the opposite sides in three collinear points.
11. The line determined by the angle bisector of an exterior angle of a triangle divides the opposite side into segments which are proportional to the adjacent sides.
12. If a diagonal of a parallelogram bisects an angle, then the parallelogram is a rhombus.
13. The median to the base of an isosceles triangle lies along the bisector of the angle opposite the base.
14. *Theorem of Ceva* In any triangle ABC, lines joining three points P_1, P_2, and P_3 on sides AB, BC, and CA, respectively, to the opposite vertices are concurrent if

$$\left(\frac{\overrightarrow{AP_1}}{\overrightarrow{P_1B}}\right)\left(\frac{\overrightarrow{BP_2}}{\overrightarrow{P_2C}}\right)\left(\frac{\overrightarrow{CP_3}}{\overrightarrow{P_3A}}\right) = 1.$$

1-7 Position Vectors

It is sometimes convenient to consider a rectangular cartesian coordinate system in discussing vectors. In three-dimensional space the position of a point P may be determined by its directed perpendicular distances from three mutually perpendicular reference planes. These planes intersect in three mutually perpendicular lines called the **coordinate axes** which are usually designated as the x-axis, y-axis, and z-axis. The three **coordinate planes** are usually designated by the pair of axes which determine the planes; that is, the xy-plane, yz-plane, and zx-plane contain the x- and y-axes, the y- and z-axes, and the z- and x-axes, respectively. An ordered triple of real numbers (a, b, c) may be associated with each point P in space such that a, b, and c represent the directed distances from the yz-, zx-, and xy-planes, respectively. The scalars a, b, and c of the ordered triple (a, b, c) are called the x-, y-, and z-coordinates, respectively, of P. We shall often speak of the ordered triple (a, b, c) as the **coordinates** of P. The point of intersection of the coordinate planes has coordinates $(0, 0, 0)$ and is called the **origin.**

It is possible to assign two different orientations to a rectangular cartesian coordinate system in space. The coordinate system is said to have a

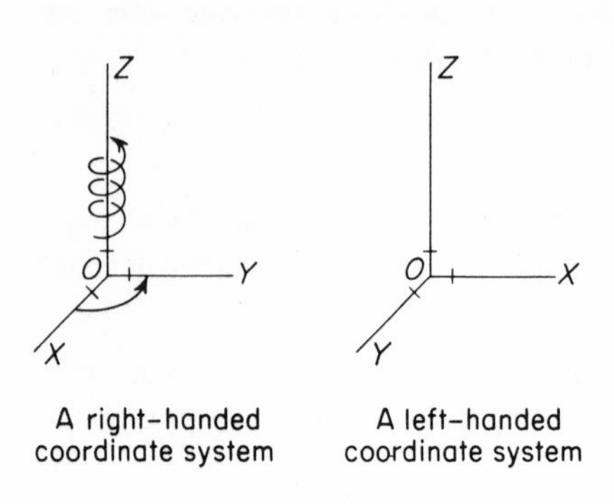

Figure 1-29

right-handed orientation if, when the positive half of the x-axis is rotated 90° onto the positive half of the y-axis, then a right-hand screw rotated in the same manner would advance along the positive half of the z-axis. A right-handed coordinate system may also be described by placing the back of a person's right hand on a table top and extending the thumb, index finger, and middle finger in three mutually perpendicular directions such that the middle finger points upward from the table top. Let the thumb, index finger, and middle finger be associated with the positive rays of the x-, y-, and z-axes, respectively. It is possible to describe a left-handed coordinate system in a similar manner with the use of a person's left hand. While both orientated coordinate systems may be used in discussing vectors in space, it is necessary to choose and use one, and only one, of the two systems since certain fundamental considerations change with orientation (See §2-6). A right-handed coordinate system will be assumed throughout our discussion of vectors.

It is convenient to choose three unit vectors, designated as $\vec{i}$, $\vec{j}$, and $\vec{k}$, with a common initial point at the origin and terminal points at (1, 0, 0), (0, 1, 0), and (0, 0, 1), respectively, as a basis for vectors in three-dimensional

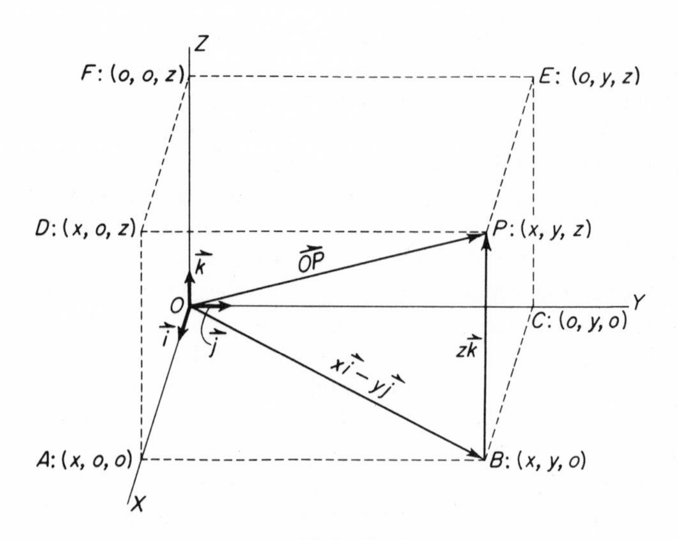

Figure 1-30

coordinate space. Note that $\vec{i}$, $\vec{j}$, and $\vec{k}$ constitute a basis since they are linearly independent. Now, with each point P: (x, y, z) in space we may associate a **position vector** $\overrightarrow{OP}$ whose initial point is the origin and whose terminal point is P. Then position vector $\overrightarrow{OP}$ may be expressed as $x\vec{i} + y\vec{j} + z\vec{k}$. Note that in Figure 1-30 the position vector $\overrightarrow{OP}$ may be associated with a diagonal of a rectangular parallelepiped whose edges are equal to $|x|$, $|y|$, and $|z|$. Therefore $|\overrightarrow{OP}|$ can be determined by using the Pythagorean theorem twice; that is,

$$\begin{aligned} |\overrightarrow{OP}|^2 &= |\overrightarrow{OB}|^2 + |\overrightarrow{BP}|^2 \\ &= |\overrightarrow{OA}|^2 + |\overrightarrow{OC}|^2 + |\overrightarrow{OF}|^2; \\ |\overrightarrow{OP}| &= \sqrt{x^2 + y^2 + z^2}. \end{aligned}$$

The real scalars x, y, and z are sometimes called the **components** of $\overrightarrow{OP}$. Since $\overrightarrow{OP}$ is a unique linear function of $\vec{i}$, $\vec{j}$, and $\vec{k}$, then *two position vectors are equal if, and only if, their corresponding components are equal.* The following theorems may be proved using the previous definitions and theorems about vectors.

Theorem 1-10 *The components of the sum (difference) of two position vectors are equal to the sum (difference) of the corresponding components of the vectors; that is, if* $\vec{a} = x_1\vec{i} + y_1\vec{j} + z_1\vec{k}$ *and* $\vec{b} = x_2\vec{i} + y_2\vec{j} + z_2\vec{k}$, *then*

$$\vec{a} \pm \vec{b} = (x_1 \pm x_2)\vec{i} + (y_1 \pm y_2)\vec{j} + (z_1 \pm z_2)\vec{k}.$$

Theorem 1-11 *The components of a scalar multiple of a position vector are equal to the scalar multiple of the corresponding components of the vector; that is, if* $\vec{a} = x\vec{i} + y\vec{j} + z\vec{k}$ *and* m *is a scalar, then* $m\vec{a} = mx\vec{i} + my\vec{j} + mz\vec{k}$.

Example 1 Determine the position vector of the point P: $(3, -4, 12)$. Find its magnitude. Determine the unit position vector in the direction of $\overrightarrow{OP}$.

The position vector of the point P: $(3, -4, 12)$ is

$$\overrightarrow{OP} = 3\vec{i} - 4\vec{j} + 12\vec{k}.$$

Its magnitude is given as

$$|\overrightarrow{OP}| = \sqrt{3^2 + (-4)^2 + 12^2} = 13.$$

The unit position vector in the direction of $\overrightarrow{OP}$ is given as

$$\frac{\overrightarrow{OP}}{|\overrightarrow{OP}|} = \frac{3}{13}\vec{i} - \frac{4}{13}\vec{j} + \frac{12}{13}\vec{k}.$$

Example 2 Determine the coordinates of the point which divides the line segment from A: $(1, -2, 0)$ to B: $(6, 8, -10)$ in the ratio 2 to 3.

Let P be the desired point. Using Theorem 1-9, $\overrightarrow{OP} = \frac{2}{5}\overrightarrow{OB} + \frac{3}{5}\overrightarrow{OA}$. Now, $\overrightarrow{OB} = 6\vec{i} + 8\vec{j} - 10\vec{k}$, and $\overrightarrow{OA} = \vec{i} - 2\vec{j}$.

Then,

$$\tfrac{2}{5}\overrightarrow{OB} = \tfrac{12}{5}\vec{i} + \tfrac{16}{5}\vec{j} - \tfrac{20}{5}\vec{k}, \qquad \text{and} \qquad \tfrac{3}{5}\overrightarrow{OA} = \tfrac{3}{5}\vec{i} - \tfrac{6}{5}\vec{j}.$$

Therefore,

$$\begin{aligned}\overrightarrow{OP} &= (\tfrac{12}{5} + \tfrac{3}{5})\vec{i} + (\tfrac{16}{5} - \tfrac{6}{5})\vec{j} + (-\tfrac{20}{5} + 0)\vec{k} \\ &= 3\vec{i} + 2\vec{j} - 4\vec{k}.\end{aligned}$$

Hence, the coordinates of P are $(3, 2, -4)$.

Example 3 Determine the two-point form of the equation of a line on a plane (Figure 1-31).

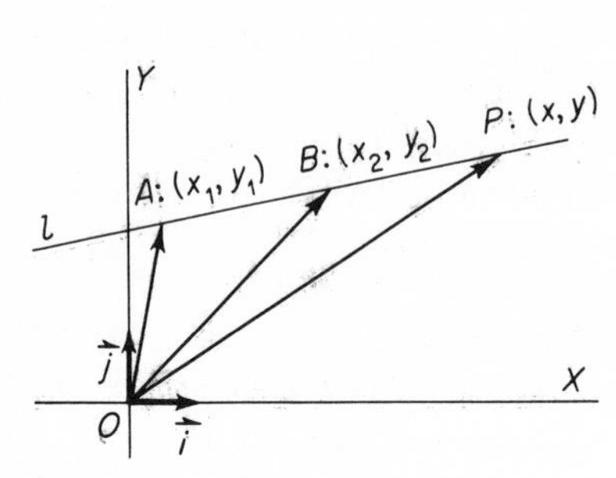

Figure 1-31

Let A: (x_1, y_1) and B: (x_2, y_2) be any two given points on line l. Let P: (x, y) be any point on line l. Since A, B, and P are collinear, then $\overrightarrow{AP} = t\overrightarrow{AB}$ for any real number t; $\overrightarrow{OP} - \overrightarrow{OA} = t(\overrightarrow{OB} - \overrightarrow{OA})$. Now, $\overrightarrow{OP} = x\vec{i} + y\vec{j}$; $\overrightarrow{OA} = x_1\vec{i} + y_1\vec{j}$; $\overrightarrow{OB} = x_2\vec{i} + y_2\vec{j}$. Therefore,

$$\begin{aligned}(x - x_1)\vec{i} &+ (y - y_1)\vec{j} \\ &= t(x_2 - x_1)\vec{i} + t(y_2 - y_1)\vec{j}.\end{aligned}$$

Since $\vec{i}$ and $\vec{j}$ are linearly independent vectors, then

$$(x - x_1) = t(x_2 - x_1), \qquad \text{and} \qquad (y - y_1) = t(y_2 - y_1)$$

represents a *parametric form* of the equation of the line with parameter t. Equating the t's in the two equations,

$$\frac{x - x_1}{x_2 - x_1} = \frac{y - y_1}{y_2 - y_1},$$

which represents the two-point form of the equation of a line through (x_1, y_1) and (x_2, y_2).

Exercises

*In Exercises 1 through 4 find (**a**) $\overrightarrow{OP}$; (**b**) $|\overrightarrow{OP}|$; (**c**) a unit position vector in the direction of $\overrightarrow{OP}$.*

1. (2, 2, 1).

2. (−3, 4, 5).

3. (3, 0, 0).

4. (1, 1, 1).

In Exercises 5 through 10 describe the locus of the points (x, y, z) *such that:*

5. $x = 0$.

6. $x = y = 0$.

7. $x = 3$.

8. $|z| < 1$.

9. $x^2 + y^2 + z^2 = 1$.

10. $|x| < \frac{1}{2}$, $|y| < \frac{1}{2}$, and $|z| < \frac{1}{2}$.

11. Determine the distance between the point P: (x, y, z) and **(a)** the xy-plane; **(b)** the x-axis.

12. Determine if the three points M: (2, 5, 9), N: (0, 1, 1), and P: (3, 7, 13) are collinear.

13. Determine if the three points M: (1, 2, 3), N: (5, 4, −2), and P: (−2, −1, 5) are collinear.

14. Given A: (3, 2, 4) and B: (5, 3, 4), show that $\overrightarrow{AB}$ is parallel to the xy-plane.

15. Given A: (3, −1, 17) and B: (8, 9, 2), find the coordinates of the point which divides the line segment AB in the ratio **(a)** 1 to 1; **(b)** 2 to 3; and **(c)** 2 to −1.

16. Find the coordinates of the centroid of the triangle with vertices A: (x_1, y_1, z_1), B: (x_2, y_2, z_2), and C: (x_3, y_3, z_3).

chapter 2

Products of Vectors

2-1 The Scalar Product

The concept of a vector as a physical quantity having magnitude and direction, or as a directed line segment, does not imply how the product of two vectors shall be defined. No *a priori* definition exists. We may arbitrarily define the multiplication of vectors in any one of several ways. The interpretation of the results of our definition may differ in some instances from the interpretation of ordinary multiplication of scalars; that is, certain algebraic properties of the algebra of real numbers may not be valid for a particular definition of the product of two vectors. The admittedly arbitrary choice of one definition over another has been motivated by heuristic considerations. That is, we choose the definition which is most suitable for the applications of the product. By studying the ways in which vector quantities are combined in physical situations, we are motivated to define two types of products. The first type of product of two vectors results in a scalar and is called the *scalar product.*

When an object is moved from a point A to a point B along a straight line, by being acted upon by a constant force $\vec{f}$ as in Figure 2-1, we are often concerned with the amount of work that is done by the force. The force $\vec{f}$ may be considered as the sum of two vectors $\vec{f}_1$ and $\vec{f}_2$ with magnitudes $|\vec{f}|\cos\theta$ and $|\vec{f}|\sin\theta$, respectively. Only the vector component whose magnitude is $|\vec{f}|\cos\theta$ results in the displacement $\vec{d}$ of the object from A to B, a distance equal to $|\vec{d}|$. The amount of work accomplished in displacing the object from A to B may be represented by the product $(|\vec{f}|\cos\theta)|\vec{d}|$.

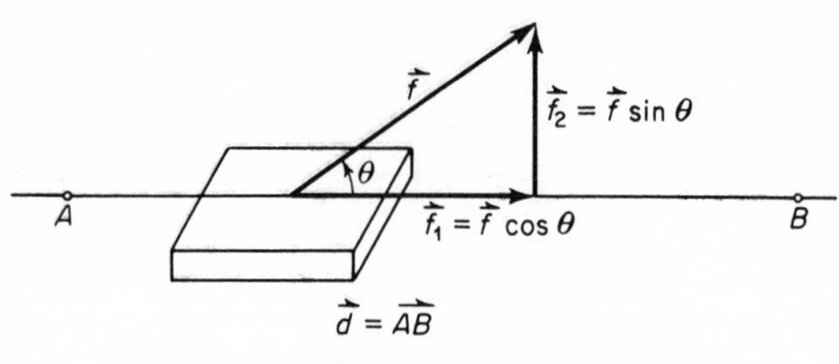

Figure 2-1

This scalar may be considered as one type of product of $\vec{f}$ and $\vec{d}$. The consideration of a number of similar physical problems suggests to us a definition for the product of two vectors.

Definition 2-1 *The* ***scalar****, or* ***dot, product*** *of two given vectors* $\vec{a}$ *and* $\vec{b}$*, designated* $\vec{a}\cdot\vec{b}$ *and read "*$\vec{a}$ *dot* $\vec{b}$*", is defined by the identity*

$$\vec{a}\cdot\vec{b} = |\vec{a}||\vec{b}| \cos(\vec{a}, \vec{b}), \tag{2-1}$$

where $(\vec{a}, \vec{b})$ *is the smallest angle between the two vectors measured (counterclockwise or clockwise) from* $\vec{a}$ *to* $\vec{b}$ *when the vectors have a common initial point; that is,* $0° \leqq |(\vec{a}, \vec{b})| \leqq 180°$.

The right-hand member of the identity (2-1) is a scalar quantity; hence the term *scalar product* of two vectors. The dot used to indicate the type of multiplication between $\vec{a}$ and $\vec{b}$ leads to the term *dot product.* Another name frequently used for the scalar product of two vectors is the **inner product.**

In Figure 2-2 it can be seen that, geometrically, $\vec{a}\cdot\vec{b}$ is equal to the product of the directed magnitude (signed length) of the projection of $\vec{a}$ onto $\vec{b}$ and the magnitude (length) of $\vec{b}$.

From the definition, the scalar product $\vec{b}\cdot\vec{a}$ is given by the expression

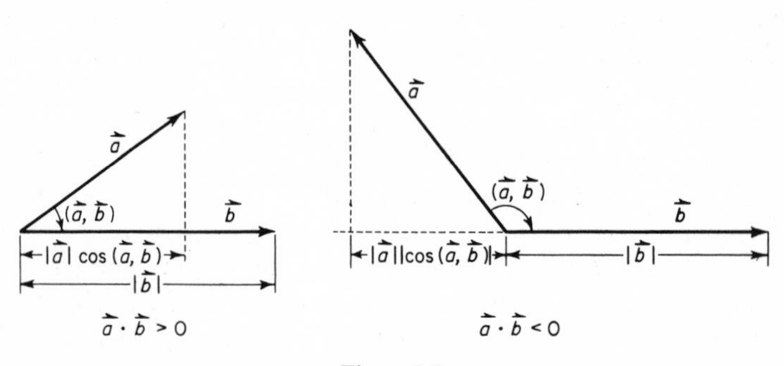

Figure 2-2

$$\vec{b}\cdot\vec{a} = |\vec{b}||\vec{a}|\cos(\vec{b}, \vec{a}). \tag{2-2}$$

Now, since angle $(\vec{b}, \vec{a})$ is the negative of angle $(\vec{a}, \vec{b})$ and $\cos(\vec{a}, \vec{b})$ equals $\cos[-(\vec{a}, \vec{b})]$, then $\cos(\vec{a}, \vec{b})$ equals $\cos(\vec{b}, \vec{a})$. Since $|\vec{a}||\vec{b}| = |\vec{b}||\vec{a}|$, the following theorem is proved.

Theorem 2-1 *The scalar product of two vectors is commutative; that is,*

$$\vec{a}\cdot\vec{b} = \vec{b}\cdot\vec{a}. \tag{2-3}$$

By the definition of the scalar product and the fact that $\cos 0° = 1$ and $\cos 90° = 0$, we may obtain the next two theorems.

Theorem 2-2 *The scalar product of a vector with itself equals the square of its magnitude; that is,*

$$\vec{a}\cdot\vec{a} = |\vec{a}|^2. \tag{2-4}$$

Theorem 2-3 *If two nonzero vectors $\vec{a}$ and $\vec{b}$ are perpendicular, then* $\vec{a}\cdot\vec{b} = 0$.

Notice that the converse of Theorem 2-3 is not necessarily true. If $\vec{a}\cdot\vec{b} = 0$, then either at least one of the vectors is a null vector, or the two nonzero vectors are perpendicular. A modified converse of Theorem 2-3 is valid, however.

Theorem 2-4 *If the scalar product of two nonzero vectors is zero, then the vectors are perpendicular.*

Since the scalar product of two vectors may be zero when neither factor is zero, division of a scalar product by a vector as an inverse process to finding the scalar product cannot be performed. Consider $\vec{a}\cdot\vec{b} = \vec{a}\cdot\vec{c}$; then $\vec{b} = \vec{c}$ may or may not be true. For example, $\vec{a}$ and $\vec{b}$ may be two nonzero perpendicular vectors and $\vec{c}$ may be a null vector. Then $\vec{a}\cdot\vec{b} = \vec{a}\cdot\vec{c}$, but $\vec{b} \neq \vec{c}$.

Theorem 2-5 *The scalar product is distributive with respect to the addition of vectors; that is,*

$$\vec{a}\cdot(\vec{b} + \vec{c}) = \vec{a}\cdot\vec{b} + \vec{a}\cdot\vec{c}. \tag{2-5}$$

Proof: Let b', c' be the signed magnitudes of the projections of $\vec{b}$ and $\vec{c}$, respectively, along $\vec{a}$, as in Figure 2-3. Then $b' + c'$ is the signed magnitude of the projection of $\vec{b} + \vec{c}$ along $\vec{a}$. The equation

$$|\vec{a}|(b' + c') = |\vec{a}|b' + |\vec{a}|c'$$

is then equivalent to $\vec{a}\cdot(\vec{b} + \vec{c}) = \vec{a}\cdot\vec{b} + \vec{a}\cdot\vec{c}$.

Theorem 2-6 *A real multiple of the scalar product of two vectors is equal to* *the scalar product of one of the vectors and the real multiple of the other; that is,*

$$m(\vec{a}\cdot\vec{b}) = (m\vec{a})\cdot\vec{b} = \vec{a}\cdot(m\vec{b}). \tag{2-6}$$

Proof:
$$\begin{aligned} m(\vec{a}\cdot\vec{b}) &= m\,|\vec{a}\,|\,|\vec{b}\,|\cos(\vec{a}, \vec{b}) \\ &= |m\vec{a}\,|\,|\vec{b}\,|\cos(m\vec{a}, \vec{b}) = (m\vec{a})\cdot\vec{b} \\ &= |\vec{a}\,|\,|m\vec{b}\,|\cos(\vec{a}, m\vec{b}) = \vec{a}\cdot(m\vec{b}). \end{aligned}$$

Any vector in space may be represented in the form $x\vec{i} + y\vec{j} + z\vec{k}$ in terms of the unit vectors $\vec{i}$ along the x-axis, $\vec{j}$ along the y-axis, and $\vec{k}$ along the z-axis. By Theorem 2-3

$$\begin{aligned} \vec{i}\cdot\vec{j} &= \vec{j}\cdot\vec{i} = 0, \\ \vec{j}\cdot\vec{k} &= \vec{k}\cdot\vec{j} = 0, \\ \vec{k}\cdot\vec{i} &= \vec{i}\cdot\vec{k} = 0. \end{aligned} \tag{2-7}$$

By Theorem 2-2

$$\begin{aligned} \vec{i}\cdot\vec{i} &= 1, \\ \vec{j}\cdot\vec{j} &= 1, \\ \vec{k}\cdot\vec{k} &= 1. \end{aligned} \tag{2-8}$$

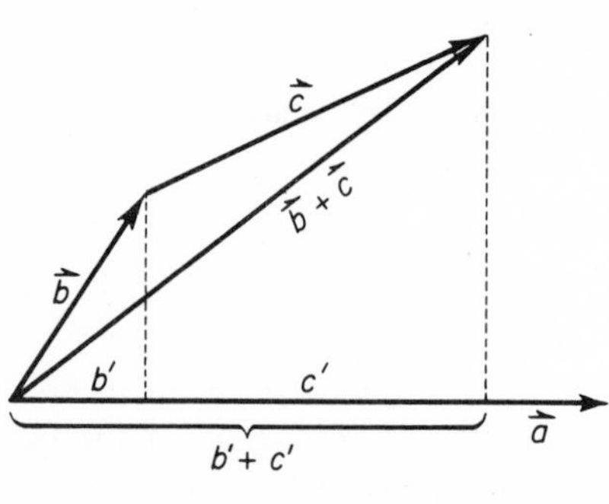

Figure 2-3

The scalar product of two position vectors may now be determined as shown in Theorem 2-7.

Theorem 2-7 *The scalar product of two position vectors is equal to the sum of the products of their corresponding components; that is, if* $\vec{a} = x_1\vec{i} + y_1\vec{j} + z_1\vec{k}$ *and* $\vec{b} = x_2\vec{i} + y_2\vec{j} + z_2\vec{k}$, *then*

$$\vec{a}\cdot\vec{b} = x_1x_2 + y_1y_2 + z_1z_2. \tag{2-9}$$

Proof: Making use of Theorems 2-1, 2-5, and 2-6,

$$\begin{aligned} \vec{a}\cdot\vec{b} &= (x_1\vec{i} + y_1\vec{j} + z_1\vec{k})\cdot(x_2\vec{i} + y_2\vec{j} + z_2\vec{k}) \\ &= x_1x_2(\vec{i}\cdot\vec{i}) + x_1y_2(\vec{i}\cdot\vec{j}) + x_1z_2(\vec{i}\cdot\vec{k}) \\ &\quad + y_1x_2(\vec{j}\cdot\vec{i}) + y_1y_2(\vec{j}\cdot\vec{j}) + y_1z_2(\vec{j}\cdot\vec{k}) \\ &\quad + z_1x_2(\vec{k}\cdot\vec{i}) + z_1y_2(\vec{k}\cdot\vec{j}) + z_1z_2(\vec{k}\cdot\vec{k}). \end{aligned}$$

But,

$$\vec{i}\cdot\vec{i} = \vec{j}\cdot\vec{j} = \vec{k}\cdot\vec{k} = 1,$$

and

$$\vec{i}\cdot\vec{j} = \vec{j}\cdot\vec{i} = \vec{j}\cdot\vec{k} = \vec{k}\cdot\vec{j} = \vec{k}\cdot\vec{i} = \vec{i}\cdot\vec{k} = 0.$$

Therefore,

$$\vec{a}\cdot\vec{b} = x_1x_2 + y_1y_2 + z_1z_2.$$

Example 1 Determine the magnitude of the position vector $\vec{a} = 4\vec{i} + 3\vec{j} + 12\vec{k}$. Then determine a unit vector in the same direction as $\vec{a}$.

By Theorem 2-2, $|\vec{a}|^2 = \vec{a}\cdot\vec{a}$. Therefore,

$$|\vec{a}| = \sqrt{\vec{a}\cdot\vec{a}} = \sqrt{(4)^2 + (3)^2 + (12)^2} = 13.$$

The unit vector in the same direction as $\vec{a}$ is that vector $\vec{u} = x\vec{i} + y\vec{j} + z\vec{k}$ such that $13\vec{u} = \vec{a}$; that is, $13(x\vec{i} + y\vec{j} + z\vec{k}) = 4\vec{i} + 3\vec{j} + 12\vec{k}$. Hence, $\vec{u} = \frac{4}{13}\vec{i} + \frac{3}{13}\vec{j} + \frac{12}{13}\vec{k}$.

Example 2 Determine the angle between the position vectors

$$\vec{a} = 3\vec{i} - 2\vec{j} + 6\vec{k},$$
$$\vec{b} = -3\vec{i} - 5\vec{j} + 8\vec{k}.$$

Let θ denote the angle between $\vec{a}$ and $\vec{b}$. By Definition 2-1, $\vec{a}\cdot\vec{b} = |\vec{a}||\vec{b}|\cos\theta$. Since neither $\vec{a}$ nor $\vec{b}$ is a null vector

$$\cos\theta = \frac{\vec{a}\cdot\vec{b}}{|\vec{a}||\vec{b}|} = \frac{(3)(-3) + (-2)(-5) + (6)(8)}{|\vec{a}||\vec{b}|} = \frac{49}{|\vec{a}||\vec{b}|}$$

where $|\vec{a}|^2 = \vec{a}\cdot\vec{a}$, and $|\vec{b}|^2 = \vec{b}\cdot\vec{b}$.

Now,

$$|\vec{a}| = \sqrt{(3)^2 + (-2)^2 + (6)^2} = 7,$$

and

$$|\vec{b}| = \sqrt{(-3)^2 + (-5)^2 + (8)^2} = 7\sqrt{2}.$$

Hence,

$$\cos\theta = \frac{49}{49\sqrt{2}} = \frac{1}{\sqrt{2}}, \qquad \text{and} \qquad \theta = 45^\circ.$$

Example 3 Find the signed magnitude of the projection of

$$\vec{a} = 3\vec{i} - \vec{j} - 2\vec{k} \text{ on } \vec{b} = \vec{i} + 2\vec{j} - 3\vec{k}.$$

The signed magnitude of the projection of $\vec{a}$ on $\vec{b}$ is equal to $|\vec{a}|\cos\theta$ and, since $|\vec{b}| \neq 0$,

$$|\vec{a}|\cos\theta = \frac{\vec{a}\cdot\vec{b}}{|\vec{b}|}.$$

Therefore,

$$|\vec{a}|\cos\theta = \frac{(3)(1) + (-1)(2) + (-2)(-3)}{\sqrt{(1)^2 + (2)^2 + (-3)^2}} = \frac{7}{\sqrt{14}} = \frac{\sqrt{14}}{2}.$$

Example 4 Verify Theorem 2-5 (the scalar product is distributive with respect to the addition of vectors) when

$$\vec{a} = 2\vec{i} - 3\vec{j} + 4\vec{k},\ \vec{b} = \vec{i} - \vec{j} + 2\vec{k}, \text{ and } \vec{c} = 3\vec{i} + 2\vec{j} + \vec{k}.$$

We evaluate and compare the two members of equation (2-5) for the given vectors $\vec{a}$, $\vec{b}$, and $\vec{c}$:

$$\begin{aligned}\vec{a}\cdot(\vec{b} + \vec{c}) &= (2\vec{i} + 3\vec{j} + 4\vec{k})\cdot[(\vec{i} - \vec{j} + 2\vec{k}) + (3\vec{i} + 2\vec{j} + \vec{k})] \\ &= (2\vec{i} - 3\vec{j} + 4\vec{k})\cdot(4\vec{i} + \vec{j} + 3\vec{k}) \\ &= (2)(4) + (-3)(1) + (4)(3) = 17;\end{aligned}$$

$$\begin{aligned}\vec{a}\cdot\vec{b} + \vec{a}\cdot\vec{c} &= (2\vec{i} - 3\vec{j} + 4\vec{k})\cdot(\vec{i} - \vec{j} + 2\vec{k}) \\ &\quad + (2\vec{i} - 3\vec{j} + 4\vec{k})\cdot(3\vec{i} + 2\vec{j} + \vec{k}) \\ &= [(2)(1) + (-3)(-1) + (4)(2)] \\ &\quad + [(2)(3) + (-3)(2) + (4)(1)] \\ &= 13 + 4 = 17.\end{aligned}$$

Hence

$$\vec{a}\cdot(\vec{b} + \vec{c}) = \vec{a}\cdot\vec{b} + \vec{a}\cdot\vec{c}.$$

Exercises

1. Determine the magnitude of the position vector $\vec{a} = 2\vec{i} + 2\vec{j} + \vec{k}$. Determine a unit vector in the same direction as $\vec{a}$.
2. Determine the angle between the position vectors $\vec{a} = 3\vec{i} - \vec{j} - 2\vec{k}$ and $\vec{b} = \vec{i} + 2\vec{j} - 3\vec{k}$.
3. Find the magnitude of the projection of the vector $\vec{a} = \vec{i} - 3\vec{j} + 2\vec{k}$ on $\vec{b} = 4\vec{i} - 3\vec{j}$.
4. Prove that if $\vec{a} = \vec{i} + 3\vec{j} - 2\vec{k}$ and $\vec{b} = \vec{i} - \vec{j} - \vec{k}$, then $\vec{a}$ and $\vec{b}$ are perpendicular.
5. Prove that **(a)** $|\vec{r}_1\cdot\vec{r}_2| \leq |\vec{r}_1||\vec{r}_2|$. State the conditions for **(b)** $\vec{r}_1\cdot\vec{r}_2 = |\vec{r}_1||\vec{r}_2|$; **(c)** $\vec{r}_1\cdot\vec{r}_2 = -|\vec{r}_1||\vec{r}_2|$.
6. Find the magnitude of the vector $x\vec{i} + y\vec{j} + z\vec{k}$.
7. Find the cosine of the angle between the diagonal of a cube and one of its edges.
8. Find: **(a)** the magnitude of $\overrightarrow{RS}$ where R: $(-1, 2, 0)$ and S: $(5, 5, 6)$; **(b)** a unit vector in the direction of $\overrightarrow{RS}$.
9. Use scalar products to prove that the triangle whose vertices are A: $(1, 0, 1)$, B: $(1, 1, 1)$, and C: $(1, 1, 0)$ is a right isosceles triangle.
10. Explain why there is not an associative law for the scalar product.
11. Prove that $\vec{a}\cdot\vec{a} = 0$ is a necessary and sufficient condition for $\vec{a}$ to be a null vector.
12. Prove that if the scalar product of a vector $\vec{a}$ with each of the three linearly independent vectors $\vec{i}$, $\vec{j}$, and $\vec{k}$ is zero, then the vector is a null vector.
13. If A, B, and C are points whose coordinates are $(1, 0, 0)$, $(0, 1, 0)$, and $(0, 0, 1)$, respectively, then find the magnitude of the projection of $\overrightarrow{AB}$ on $\overrightarrow{AC}$.

2-2 Applications of the Scalar Product

Many theorems in elementary plane geometry, trigonometry, and analytic geometry have exceedingly simple vector proofs. In this selection the proofs of several such theorems shall be illustrated. Vector proofs involving the scalar product usually involve one of two special cases: the first, when the vectors are nonzero perpendicular vectors, in which case the scalar product is zero (Theorem 2-3); the second, when the vectors are equal, in which case the scalar product is equal to the square of the magnitude of the vector (Theorem 2-2).

Example 1 If the diagonals of a parallelogram are perpendicular, then the parallelogram is a rhombus (Figure 2-4).

Let $ABCD$ be a parallelogram. Let $\vec{a}$ and $\vec{b}$ be associated with the adjacent sides AB and BC, respectively. Then $\vec{a} + \vec{b}$ and $\vec{a} - \vec{b}$ are vectors associated with the diagonals. If the diagonals are perpendicular, then $(\vec{a} + \vec{b})\cdot(\vec{a} - \vec{b}) = 0$. However,

$$\begin{aligned}(\vec{a} + \vec{b})\cdot(\vec{a} - \vec{b}) &= (\vec{a} + \vec{b})\cdot\vec{a} - (\vec{a} + \vec{b})\cdot\vec{b} \\ &= \vec{a}\cdot\vec{a} + \vec{b}\cdot\vec{a} - \vec{a}\cdot\vec{b} - \vec{b}\cdot\vec{b} \\ &= \vec{a}\cdot\vec{a} - \vec{b}\cdot\vec{b} \qquad (\text{since } \vec{b}\cdot\vec{a} = \vec{a}\cdot\vec{b}) \\ &= |\vec{a}|^2 - |\vec{b}|^2.\end{aligned}$$

Therefore, $|\vec{a}|^2 - |\vec{b}|^2 = 0$, or $|\vec{a}| = |\vec{b}|$. Hence, two adjacent sides of the parallelogram are equal, and the parallelogram is a rhombus.

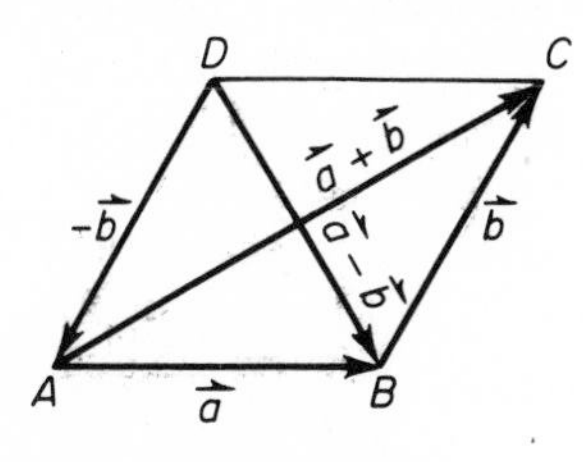

Figure 2-4

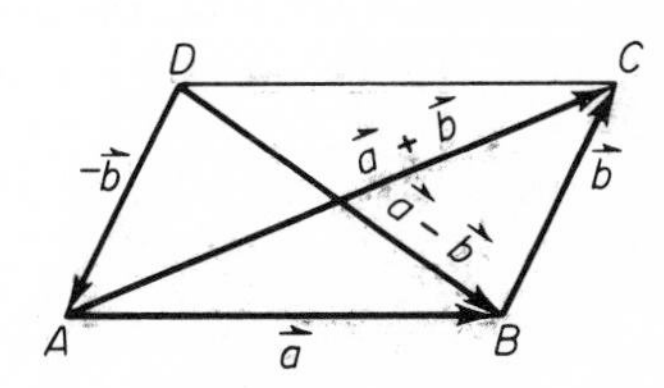

Figure 2-5

Example 2 The sum of the squares of the diagonals of any parallelogram is equal to the sum of the squares of the sides (Figure 2-5).

Let $ABCD$ be any parallelogram. Let $\vec{a}$ and $\vec{b}$ be associated with the adjacent sides AB and BC, respectively. Then $\overrightarrow{AC}$ and $\overrightarrow{DB}$ are vectors associated with the diagonals where $\overrightarrow{AC} = \vec{a} + \vec{b}$ and $\overrightarrow{DB} = \vec{a} - \vec{b}$. Now,

$$\overrightarrow{AC}\cdot\overrightarrow{AC} = (\vec{a} + \vec{b})\cdot(\vec{a} + \vec{b})$$

$$|\overrightarrow{AC}|^2 = |\vec{a}|^2 + |\vec{b}|^2 + 2\vec{a}\cdot\vec{b}$$

and

$$\overrightarrow{DB}\cdot\overrightarrow{DB} = (\vec{a} - \vec{b})\cdot(\vec{a} - \vec{b})$$

$$|\overrightarrow{DB}|^2 = |\vec{a}|^2 + |\vec{b}|^2 - 2\vec{a}\cdot\vec{b}.$$

Therefore,

$$|\overrightarrow{AC}|^2 + |\overrightarrow{DB}|^2 = 2|\vec{a}|^2 + 2|\vec{b}|^2.$$

Since

$$|\vec{a}| = |\overrightarrow{AB}| = |\overrightarrow{CD}|, \text{ and } |\vec{b}| = |\overrightarrow{BC}| = |\overrightarrow{DA}|,$$

then

$$|\overrightarrow{AC}|^2 + |\overrightarrow{DB}|^2 = |\overrightarrow{AB}|^2 + |\overrightarrow{CD}|^2 + |\overrightarrow{BC}|^2 + |\overrightarrow{DA}|^2;$$

that is, the sum of the squares of the diagonals of any parallelogram is equal to the sum of the squares of the sides.

Example 3 An angle inscribed in a semicircle is a right angle (Figure 2-6).

Consider the semicircle ACB with center at O where the points A, B, C, and O do not pairwise coincide. Associate vectors $\vec{a}$ and $\vec{c}$ with radii OA and OC, respectively. Then the vectors $-\vec{a}$, $\vec{a} - \vec{c}$, and $-\vec{a} - \vec{c}$ may be associated with the line segments OB, CA, and CB, respectively. Now,

$$(\vec{a} - \vec{c})\cdot(-\vec{a} - \vec{c}) = -\vec{a}\cdot\vec{a} - \vec{a}\cdot\vec{c} + \vec{c}\cdot\vec{a} + \vec{c}\cdot\vec{c} = |\vec{c}|^2 - |\vec{a}|^2.$$

But $|\vec{c}| = |\vec{a}|$, since the radii of the same circle are equal. Hence $(\vec{a} - \vec{c})\cdot(-\vec{a} - \vec{c}) = 0$. It follows that the line segments CA and CB associated with these vectors are perpendicular, or C coincides with A or B. Therefore, the angle inscribed in a semicircle is a right angle.

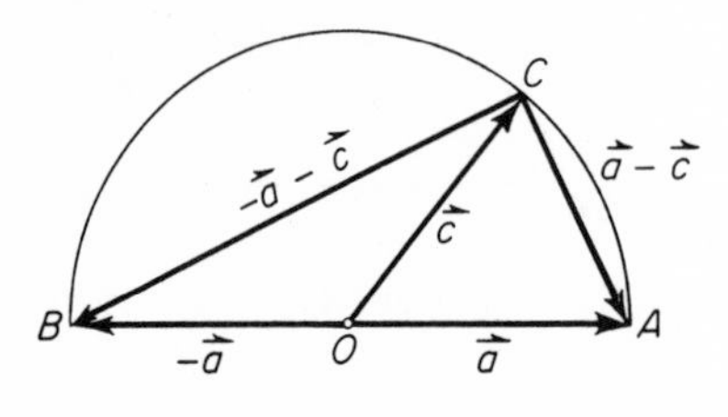

Figure 2-6

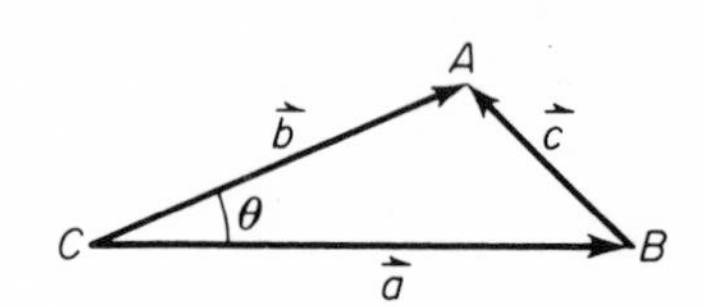

Figure 2-7

Example 4 Derive the law of cosines (Figure 2-7).

Let ABC be any triangle. Associate $\vec{a}$, $\vec{b}$, and $\vec{c}$ with sides CB, CA, and BA, respectively. Denote angle ACB by θ. Now,

$$\vec{c} = \vec{b} - \vec{a}$$

and

$$\vec{c}\cdot\vec{c} = (\vec{b} - \vec{a})\cdot(\vec{b} - \vec{a})$$
$$= (\vec{b} - \vec{a})\cdot\vec{b} - (\vec{b} - \vec{a})\cdot\vec{a}$$
$$= \vec{b}\cdot\vec{b} - \vec{a}\cdot\vec{b} - \vec{b}\cdot\vec{a} + \vec{a}\cdot\vec{a}.$$

Then

$$|\vec{c}|^2 = |\vec{b}|^2 + |\vec{a}|^2 - 2\vec{a}\cdot\vec{b} \qquad (\text{since } \vec{b}\cdot\vec{a} = \vec{a}\cdot\vec{b})$$
$$= |\vec{b}|^2 + |\vec{a}|^2 - 2|\vec{a}||\vec{b}|\cos\theta.$$

Example 5 The median to the base of an isosceles triangle is perpendicular to the base (Figure 2-8).

Consider an isosceles triangle ABC with M the mid-point of the base AB. Associate $\vec{a}$, $\vec{b}$, and $\vec{m}$ with equal sides CA, CB and median CM, respectively. Side AB may now be associated with $\vec{b} - \vec{a}$. Now,

$$\vec{b} - \vec{m} = \tfrac{1}{2}(\vec{b} - \vec{a})$$
$$\vec{m} = \tfrac{1}{2}(\vec{b} + \vec{a}).$$

Then

$$\vec{m}\cdot(\vec{b} - \vec{a}) = \tfrac{1}{2}(\vec{b} + \vec{a})\cdot(\vec{b} - \vec{a})$$
$$= \tfrac{1}{2}(|\vec{b}|^2 - |\vec{a}|^2).$$

Since sides CA and CB are equal, $|\vec{a}| = |\vec{b}|$, $|\vec{b}|^2 - |\vec{a}|^2 = 0$, and $\vec{m}\cdot(\vec{b} - \vec{a}) = 0$. Therefore, $\vec{m}$ is perpendicular to $\vec{b} - \vec{a}$ since $|\vec{m}| \neq 0$ and $|\vec{b} - \vec{a}| \neq 0$; that is, the median CM is perpendicular to side AB.

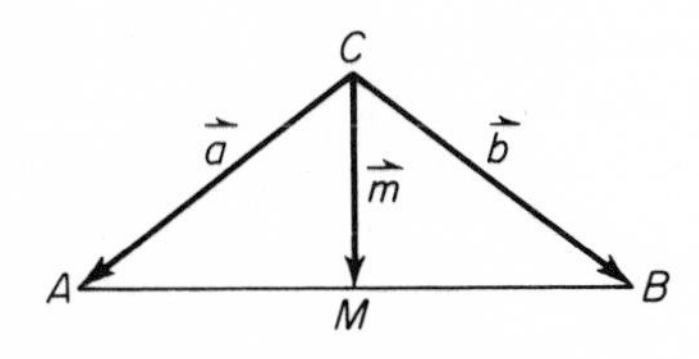

Figure 2-8

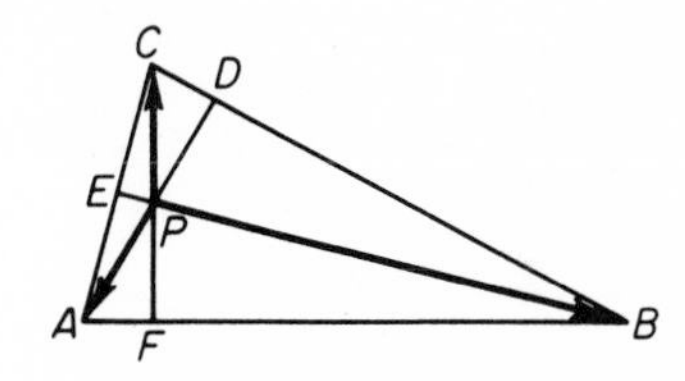

Figure 2-9

Example 6 The altitudes of any triangle are concurrent (Figure 2-9).

If ABC is a right triangle, the theorem is obviously true. Let ABC be any triangle, other than right triangle, with altitudes AD and BE intersecting at point P. Let F be the point of intersection of line CP and side AB. Then

$$\overrightarrow{PB}\cdot(\overrightarrow{PC} - \overrightarrow{PA}) = 0, \qquad \text{and} \qquad \overrightarrow{PA}\cdot(\overrightarrow{PB} - \overrightarrow{PC}) = 0.$$

Therefore,

$$\overrightarrow{PB}\cdot(\overrightarrow{PC} - \overrightarrow{PA}) + \overrightarrow{PA}\cdot(\overrightarrow{PB} - \overrightarrow{PC}) = 0$$
$$\overrightarrow{PB}\cdot\overrightarrow{PC} - \overrightarrow{PA}\cdot\overrightarrow{PC} = 0$$

$$(\overrightarrow{PB} - \overrightarrow{PA}) \cdot \overrightarrow{PC} = 0$$
$$\overrightarrow{AB} \cdot \overrightarrow{PC} = 0.$$

Since $|\overrightarrow{AB}| \neq 0$ and $|\overrightarrow{PC}| \neq 0$, the line PC is perpendicular to side AB; that is, line segment CF is the altitude to side AB and contains the point P, the point of intersection of the other two altitudes. Hence, the altitudes of any triangle are concurrent.

Notice that the proofs of the theorems in Examples 1 through 6 involved the use of vectors that were not expressed with reference to a coordinate system. The following examples make use of the concept of the scalar product of two position vectors.

Example 7 Prove that $\cos(\theta - \phi) = \cos\theta \cos\phi + \sin\theta \sin\phi$ (Figure 2-10).

Let $\vec{a}$ and $\vec{b}$ be unit position vectors on a cartesian coordinate plane, such that the vectors $\vec{a}$ and $\vec{b}$ form angles θ and ϕ, respectively, with the positive half of the x-axis. Then $\vec{a} = \cos\theta\,\vec{i} + \sin\theta\,\vec{j}$ and $\vec{b} = \cos\phi\,\vec{i} + \sin\phi\,\vec{j}$. Now by Definition 2-1,

$$\vec{a} \cdot \vec{b} = |\vec{a}||\vec{b}| \cos(\vec{a}, \vec{b}) = |\vec{a}||\vec{b}| \cos(\phi - \theta)$$
$$= |\vec{a}||\vec{b}| \cos(\theta - \phi) = \cos(\theta - \phi).$$

Note that we may consider $\vec{a}$ and $\vec{b}$ as vectors in space whose third components are zero. By Theorem 2-7 the scalar product of the unit position vectors $\vec{a}$ and $\vec{b}$ may be expressed as

$$\vec{a} \cdot \vec{b} = \cos\theta \cos\phi + \sin\theta \sin\phi.$$

Hence,

$$\cos(\theta - \phi) = \cos\theta \cos\phi + \sin\theta \sin\phi.$$

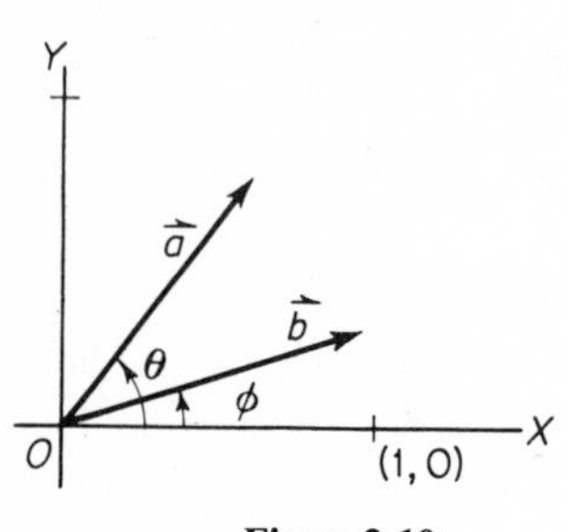

Figure 2-10

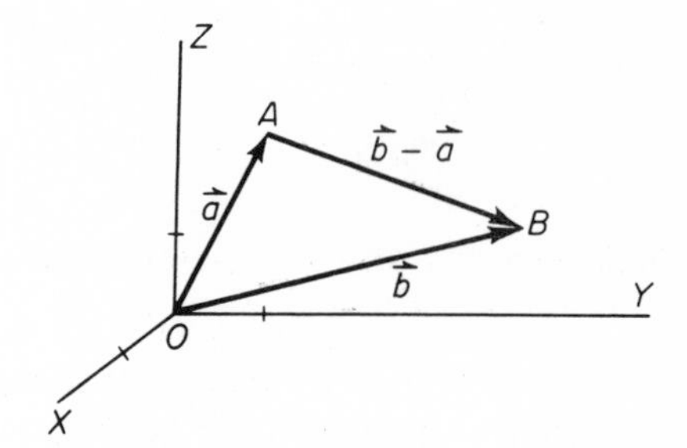

Figure 2-11

Example 8 Determine a formula for the distance between two points in space (Figure 2-11).

Let A: (x_1, y_1, z_1) and B: (x_2, y_2, z_2) be any two points in space with position vectors $\vec{a}$ and $\vec{b}$. Then $\vec{a} = x_1\vec{i} + y_1\vec{j} + z_1\vec{k}$, $\vec{b} = x_2\vec{i} + y_2\vec{j}$

$+ z_2\vec{k}$, and $\overrightarrow{AB} = \vec{b} - \vec{a}$. The distance between A and B equals $|\vec{b} - \vec{a}|$. Now,

$$\vec{b} - \vec{a} = (x_2 - x_1)\vec{i} + (y_2 - y_1)\vec{j} + (z_2 - z_1)\vec{k}.$$

According to Theorem 2-2,

$$|\vec{b} - \vec{a}| = \sqrt{(\vec{b} - \vec{a})\cdot(\vec{b} - \vec{a})} \tag{2-10}$$

represents the vector formula for the distance between two points in space. Since

$$(\vec{b} - \vec{a})\cdot(\vec{b} - \vec{a}) = (x_2 - x_1)^2 + (y_2 - y_1)^2 + (z_2 - z_1)^2,$$

$$|\vec{b} - \vec{a}| = \sqrt{(x_2 - x_1)^2 + (y_2 - y_1)^2 + (z_2 - z_1)^2} \tag{2-11}$$

represents the cartesian coordinate formula for the distance between two points (x_1, y_1, z_1) and (x_2, y_2, z_2).

Other applications of the scalar product shall be considered in subsequent sections of this chapter. In Chapter 3 the use of the scalar product, along with other concepts to be developed in the present chapter, shall be considered as they apply to the study of the coordinate geometry of planes and lines in three-dimensional space.

Exercises

Make use of the concept of the scalar product of two vectors to prove the theorems stated in Exercises 1 through 11.

1. The diagonals of a rhombus are perpendicular.
2. In any right triangle the square of the hypotenuse is equal to the sum of the squares of the other two sides (*Pythagorean Theorem*).
3. In any right triangle the median to the hypotenuse is equal to one-half the hypotenuse.
4. The line segments joining consecutive mid-points of the sides of any square form a square.
5. The sum of the squares of the diagonals of any quadrilateral is equal to twice the sum of the squares of the line segments joining the mid-points of the opposite sides.
6. If, from a point outside any circle, a tangent and a secant through the diameter are drawn, then the tangent is the mean proportional between the secant and its external segment.
7. $\cos(\theta + \phi) = \cos\theta\cos\phi - \sin\theta\sin\phi$.
8. If a line is perpendicular to two intersecting lines at their point of intersection, then the line is perpendicular to the plane determined by the intersecting lines.

9. For any triangle ABC, $|\overrightarrow{AB}| = |\overrightarrow{AC}| \cos A + |\overrightarrow{BC}| \cos B$.

10. The perpendicular bisectors of the sides of a triangle are concurrent.

2-3 Circles and Lines on a Coordinate Plane

In analytic geometry many properties and equations related to the circle and the line may be derived by vector methods. In this section a selection of those properties and equations whose derivations may be obtained by use of the scalar product are illustrated through a sequence of examples.

Example 1 Determine the equation of a circle with center at C: (x_1, y_1) and radius a (Figure 2-12).

Let P: (x, y) be any point on the circle with center at C: (x_1, y_1) and radius a. Then $|\overrightarrow{CP}| = a$, and

$$\overrightarrow{CP} \cdot \overrightarrow{CP} = a^2 \tag{2-12}$$

represents a vector form of the equation of the circle. Since $\overrightarrow{CP} = \overrightarrow{OP} - \overrightarrow{OC}$,

$$(\overrightarrow{OP} - \overrightarrow{OC}) \cdot (\overrightarrow{OP} - \overrightarrow{OC}) = a^2 \tag{2-13}$$

also represents a vector form of the equation of the circle. Now $\overrightarrow{OP} = x\vec{i} + y\vec{j}$, $\overrightarrow{OC} = x_1\vec{i} + y_1\vec{j}$, and $\overrightarrow{CP} = \overrightarrow{OP} - \overrightarrow{OC} = (x - x_1)\vec{i} + (y - y_1)\vec{j}$. Hence by (2-12),

$$(x - x_1)^2 + (y - y_1)^2 = a^2 \tag{2-14}$$

represents a rectangular cartesian coordinate form of the equation of a circle with center at C: (x_1, y_1) and radius a.

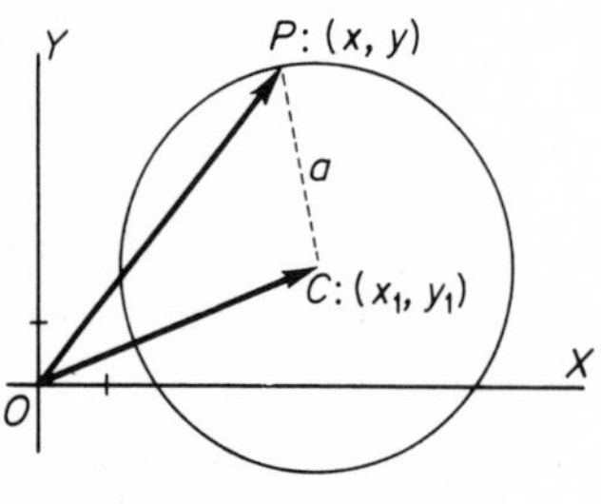

Figure 2-12

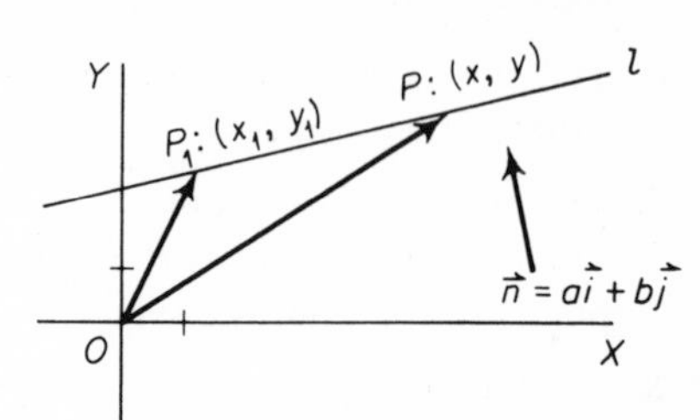

Figure 2-13

Example 2 Determine the equation of the line l passing through a given point P_1: (x_1, y_1) and perpendicular to a given vector $\vec{n} = a\vec{i} + b\vec{j}$ (Figure 2-13).

Let P: (x, y) be a general point on the line l. Then $\overrightarrow{OP} - \overrightarrow{OP_1}$ is perpendicular (normal) to $\vec{n}$, and

$$(\overrightarrow{OP} - \overrightarrow{OP_1})\cdot\vec{n} = 0 \tag{2-15}$$

represents a vector form of the equation of line l. Since $\overrightarrow{OP} = x\vec{i} + y\vec{j}$, $\overrightarrow{OP_1} = x_1\vec{i} + y_1\vec{j}$, and $\vec{n} = a\vec{i} + b\vec{j}$, then

$$\overrightarrow{OP} - \overrightarrow{OP_1} = (x - x_1)\vec{i} + (y - y_1)\vec{j}$$

and

$$(\overrightarrow{OP} - \overrightarrow{OP_1})\cdot\vec{n} = a(x - x_1) + b(y - y_1).$$

Therefore,

$$a(x - x_1) + b(y - y_1) = 0 \tag{2-16}$$

represents a rectangular cartesian coordinate form of the equation of the line l. Note that the coefficients of x and y are the horizontal and vertical components of the vector normal to the line. We shall make use of this fact in the next two examples.

Example 3 Determine a formula for the distance r between a point P_1: (x_1, y_1) and a line $ax + by + c = 0$ (Figure 2-14).

Note that the distance between a point P_1 and a given line is defined to be the shortest distance, and is measured along the line through P_1 perpendicular to the given line. Let P_0: (x_0, y_0) be any point on the given line; then, $ax_0 + by_0 + c = 0$. Let $\vec{n}$ be any vector normal to the line, such as $a\vec{i} + b\vec{j}$. Then the distance r is the magnitude of the projection of $\overrightarrow{P_0P_1}$ on $\vec{n}$ and, as in Example 3 of §2-1,

$$r = \frac{|\overrightarrow{P_0P_1}\cdot\vec{n}|}{|\vec{n}|}. \tag{2-17}$$

Since $\overrightarrow{P_0P_1} = (x_1 - x_0)\vec{i} + (y_1 - y_0)\vec{j}$, and $\vec{n} = a\vec{i} + b\vec{j}$, then

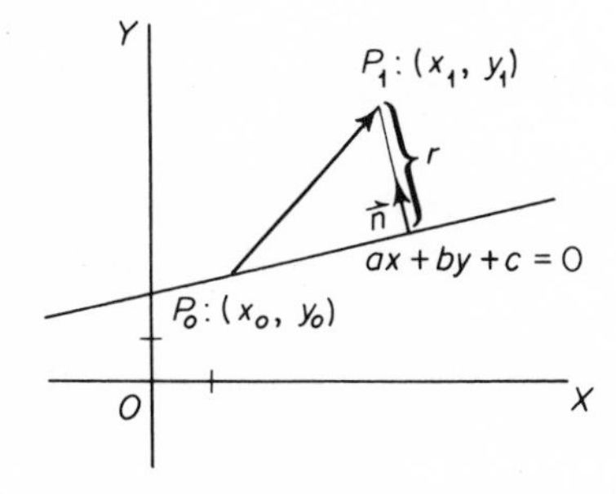

Figure 2-14

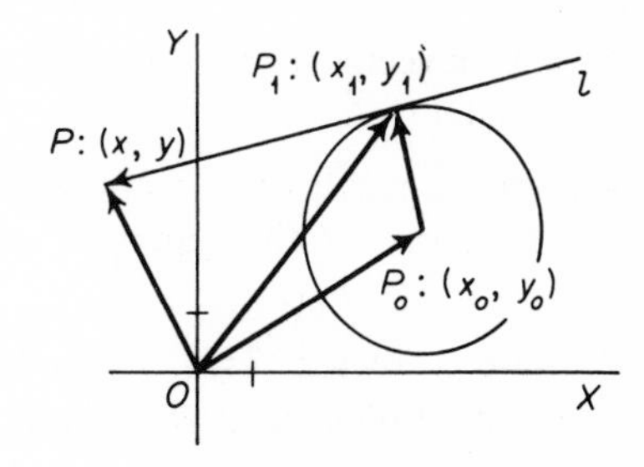

Figure 2-15

$$r = \frac{|a(x_1 - x_0) + b(y_1 - y_0)|}{\sqrt{a^2 + b^2}}.$$

Now, $-ax_0 - by_0 = c$. Therefore,

$$r = \frac{|ax_1 + by_1 + c|}{\sqrt{a^2 + b^2}}. \tag{2-18}$$

Example 4 Determine the equation of the line l, tangent at P_1: (x_1, y_1) to the circle whose center is P_0: (x_0, y_0) (Figure 2-15).

Let P: (x, y) be a general point on the tangent line l. Line l is tangent to the circle if, and only if, $\overrightarrow{P_1P}$ is perpendicular to $\overrightarrow{P_0P_1}$, the radius vector to the tangent. Therefore,

$$\overrightarrow{P_1P} \cdot \overrightarrow{P_0P_1} = 0 \tag{2-19}$$

and

$$(\overrightarrow{OP} - \overrightarrow{OP_1}) \cdot (\overrightarrow{OP_1} - \overrightarrow{OP_0}) = 0 \tag{2-20}$$

represent vector forms of the tangent line l. Since $\overrightarrow{P_1P} = (x - x_1)\vec{i} + (y - y_1)\vec{j}$ and $\overrightarrow{P_0P_1} = (x_1 - x_0)\vec{i} + (y_1 - y_0)\vec{j}$, then

$$(x - x_1)(x_1 - x_0) + (y - y_1)(y_1 - y_0) = 0 \tag{2-21}$$

represents a rectangular cartesian coordinate form of the equation of the line l, tangent at P_1: (x_1, y_1) to the circle whose center is P_0: (x_0, y_0).

Exercises

1. Determine the equation of a circle with center at C: $(1, -3)$ and radius 4.
2. Determine the equation of the line passing through P_1: $(2, 1)$ and perpendicular to $\vec{n} = 3\vec{i} - \vec{j}$.
3. Find the distance from P_1: $(3, 2)$ to the line $3x + 4y - 7 = 0$.
4. Determine the equation of the line tangent at P_1: $(5, 1)$ to the circle whose center is P_0: $(3, -2)$.
5. State a vector form of the equation of the straight line through the origin parallel to $\vec{b}$.
6. Use the result of Exercise 5 to determine a rectangular cartesian coordinate form of the equation of the line through the origin parallel to $\vec{b} = b_1\vec{i} + b_2\vec{j}$.
7. State a vector form of the equation of the straight line through the terminal point of $\vec{a}$ and parallel to $\vec{b}$.
8. Use the result of Exercise 7 to determine a rectangular cartesian coordinate form of the equation of the line through (a_1, a_2) parallel to $\vec{b} = b_1\vec{i} + b_2\vec{j}$.
9. Find a formula for the distance r from the origin to the line $ax + by + c = 0$.

2-4 Translation and Rotation

It is often desirable or necessary to change the position of a coordinate system relative to particular geometric figures in order to improve the efficiency of the system. A change of the positions of the axes of a rectangular cartesian coordinate system which results in another rectangular cartesian coordinate system, which preserves distance, is called a **rigid motion transformation** of the coordinate system. Two such rigid motion transformations in the plane are discussed in this section.

A transformation which maps the x- and y-axes onto new axes, denoted by x' and y', parallel to and oriented as the original x- and y-axes, respectively, is called a **translation** of the coordinate axes. Let the origin O' of the $x'y'$-coordinate system be located at the point (h, k) in the xy-system. The relation between the $x'y'$-coordinates and the xy-coordinates of any point P in the plane may be determined by vector methods. Now $\overrightarrow{OP} = \overrightarrow{OO'} + \overrightarrow{O'P}$ (Figure 2-16). Therefore

$$\begin{aligned} x\vec{i} + y\vec{j} &= (h\vec{i} + k\vec{j}) + (x'\vec{i} + y'\vec{j}) \\ &= (x' + h)\vec{i} + (y' + k)\vec{j}. \end{aligned}$$

Since $\vec{i}$ and $\vec{j}$ are linearly independent vectors,

$$\begin{cases} x = x' + h, \\ y = y' + k. \end{cases} \tag{2-22}$$

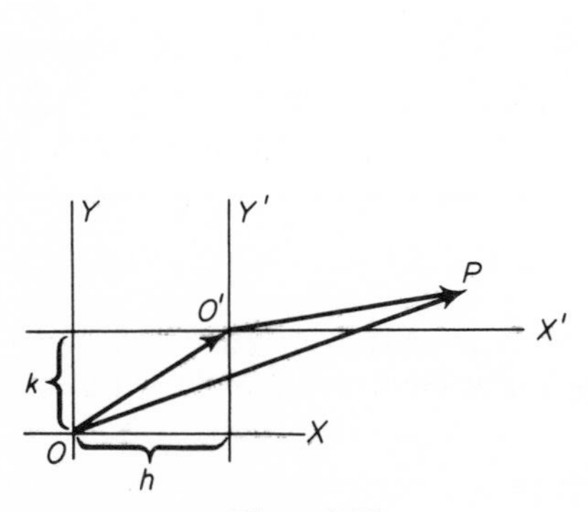

Figure 2-16

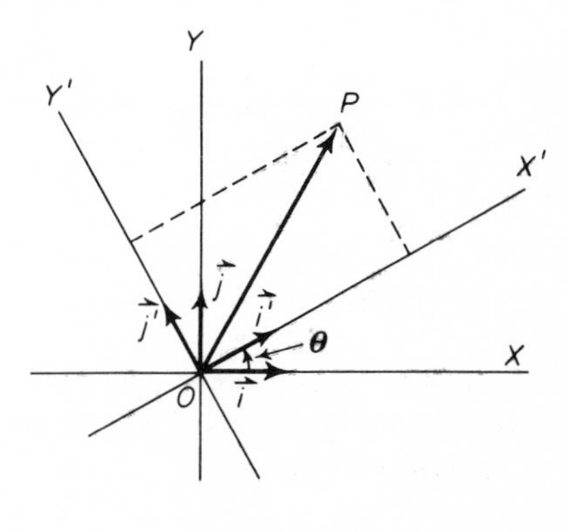

Figure 2-17

Example 1 Determine the equation of $x^2 - 6x + y^2 - 8y + 9 = 0$ in the $x'y'$-system obtained by a translation of axes such that the point $(3, 4)$ becomes the new origin.

By the equations (2-22), $x = x' + 3$ and $y = y' + 4$. Then $(x' + 3)^2 - 6(x' + 3) + (y' + 4)^2 - 8(y' + 4) + 9 = 0$; that is, $(x')^2 + (y')^2 = 16$.

Consider a transformation whereby the x'- and y'-axes are obtained by rotating the x- and y-axes through a positive angle θ about the origin. Such a transformation is called a **rotation** of the coordinate axes about the origin. Note that in this case the origins of the $x'y'$- and xy-systems coincide. Let P be any point in the plane with coordinates (x', y') and (x, y) in the $x'y'$- and xy-systems, respectively. Now, as in Figure 2-17,

$$\overrightarrow{OP} = x\vec{i} + y\vec{j} = x'\vec{i}' + y'\vec{j}',$$

where $\vec{i}' = \cos\theta\,\vec{i} + \sin\theta\,\vec{j}$ and $\vec{j}' = \cos(\theta + 90°)\vec{i} + \sin(\theta + 90°)\vec{j}$. Therefore,

$$\begin{aligned} x\vec{i} + y\vec{j} &= [x'\cos\theta + y'\cos(\theta + 90°)]\vec{i} + [x'\sin\theta + y'\sin(\theta + 90°)]\vec{j} \\ &= [x'\cos\theta - y'\sin\theta]\vec{i} + [x'\sin\theta + y'\cos\theta]\vec{j}. \end{aligned}$$

Hence,

$$\begin{cases} x = x'\cos\theta - y'\sin\theta, \\ y = x'\sin\theta + y'\cos\theta. \end{cases} \tag{2-23}$$

Example 2 Determine the new equation of the graph of $xy = 4$ in the $x'y'$-system obtained by a rotation of axes through 45°.

Using the equations (2-23) with $\theta = 45°$,

$$\begin{cases} x = \dfrac{1}{\sqrt{2}}x' - \dfrac{1}{\sqrt{2}}y', \\ y = \dfrac{1}{\sqrt{2}}x' + \dfrac{1}{\sqrt{2}}y'; \end{cases}$$

and substituting for x and y in the given equation $xy = 4$:

$$\begin{aligned} \left(\frac{1}{\sqrt{2}}x' - \frac{1}{\sqrt{2}}y'\right)\left(\frac{1}{\sqrt{2}}x' + \frac{1}{\sqrt{2}}y'\right) &= 4 \\ \tfrac{1}{2}(x')^2 - \tfrac{1}{2}(y')^2 &= 4 \\ (x')^2 - (y')^2 &= 8. \end{aligned}$$

Exercises

In Exercises 1 through 4 find the new coordinates of each given point after a translation of the coordinate axes, such that the new origin is at (3, −2) in the original system.

1. (5, 3). **2.** (0, 0).

3. (−2, 1). **4.** (3, −2).

5. Find equations expressing the new coordinates (x', y') of a point (x, y) in terms of x and y after a rotation of the coordinate axes about the origin through an angle θ.

In Exercises 6 through 9, find the new coordinates of each given point after a rotation of the coordinates axes about the origin through the stated angle. Use the results obtained in Exercise 5.

6. (3, 0); 60°. **7.** $(2, \sqrt{3})$; 30°.

8. $(1, 2); -90°$.

9. $(-2, 2); 135°$.

In Exercises 10 through 12, determine the new equation of the graph of each equation after a translation of axes, so that the given point is the new origin.

10. $x + 3y + 6 = 0; (0, -2)$.

11. $x^2 - 2y + 6x + 8 = 0; (-3, 4)$.

12. $9x^2 + 4y^2 + 18x + 24y + 9 = 0; (-1, -3)$.

In Exercises 13 through 15 determine the new equations of the graph of each equation after a rotation of axes about the origin through the angle θ.

13. $\sqrt{2}\,x + \sqrt{2}\,y + 5 = 0; \theta = 45°$.

14. $x^2 - y^2 - 10 = 0; \theta = 90°$.

15. $7x^2 - 6\sqrt{3}\,xy + 13y^2 - 16 = 0; \theta = 30°$.

16. Find the new coordinates of the point $(3, 4)$ if the axes are translated, so that the origin is the point whose coordinates were $(2, -3)$, and then the axes are rotated $60°$ about the new origin.

17. Change the order of the transformations in Exercise 16 and determine the new coordinates of the point.

18. A rotation of the coordinate axes about the origin transforms an equation of the form

$$Ax^2 + Bxy + Cy^2 + Dx + Ey + F = 0$$

into an equation of the form

$$A'x'^2 + B'x'y' + C'y'^2 + D'x' + E'y' + F' = 0.$$

Show that

$$B'^2 - 4A'C' = B^2 - 4AC.$$

In Exercises 19 and 20, determine a rotation of the coordinate axes about the origin which makes the $x'y'$ term vanish.

19. $x^2 + xy + y^2 = 8$.

20. $8x^2 - 12xy + 17y^2 + 2x + y = 20$.

21. Determine a rotation of the coordinate axes about the origin which makes $B' = 0$ in Exercise 18.

2-5 Orthogonal Bases

Two nonzero vectors $\overrightarrow{x_1}$ and $\overrightarrow{x_2}$ such that $\overrightarrow{x_1}\cdot\overrightarrow{x_2} = 0$ are called **orthogonal vectors.** A set of two such vectors constitutes an **orthogonal basis** for a vector space of two dimensions. Three nonzero vectors $\overrightarrow{x_1}$, $\overrightarrow{x_2}$, and $\overrightarrow{x_3}$, such that $\overrightarrow{x_m}\cdot\overrightarrow{x_n} = 0$ for all pairs m, n where $m \neq n$, is a set of three orthogonal vectors which constitutes an orthogonal basis for a vector space of three dimensions. The set of vectors $\vec{i}$, $\vec{j}$, and $\vec{k}$ is an example of a set of three orthogonal vectors. Since each of these vectors is a unit vector, the set constitutes a **normal orthogonal basis**, sometimes called an **orthonormal basis.**

It is often necessary to determine an orthogonal or orthonormal basis for a vector space of two dimensions embedded in a vector space of three dimensions. If $\vec{y_1}$ and $\vec{y_2}$ are two independent three-dimensional vectors, it is possible to determine two orthogonal vectors $\vec{x_1}$ and $\vec{x_2}$ in the two-dimensional vector space **spanned** by $\vec{y_1}$ and $\vec{y_2}$ (that is, for which $\vec{y_1}$ and $\vec{y_2}$ is a basis) by means of the following process: First, let $\vec{x_1} = \vec{y_1}$ and $\vec{x_2} = \vec{y_1} + t\vec{y_2}$. Then t is determined such that $\vec{x_1}\cdot\vec{x_2} = 0$:

$$\vec{y_1}\cdot(\vec{y_1} + t\vec{y_2}) = 0,$$

$$(\vec{y_1}\cdot\vec{y_1}) + t(\vec{y_1}\cdot\vec{y_2}) = 0,$$

$$t = -\frac{\vec{y_1}\cdot\vec{y_1}}{\vec{y_1}\cdot\vec{y_2}},$$

and

$$\vec{x_2} = \vec{y_1} - \frac{\vec{y_1}\cdot\vec{y_1}}{\vec{y_1}\cdot\vec{y_2}}\vec{y_2}. \tag{2-24}$$

Therefore $\vec{y_1}$ and

$$\vec{y_1} - \frac{\vec{y_1}\cdot\vec{y_1}}{\vec{y_1}\cdot\vec{y_2}}\vec{y_2}$$

constitute an orthogonal basis for the vector space spanned by $\vec{y_1}$ and $\vec{y_2}$. An orthonormal basis may be obtained by multiplying each vector by the reciprocal of its magnitude. The process that has been used is an elementary example of a more general process, called the **Gram-Schmidt process,** for finding orthogonal bases; this process finds application in the study of n-dimensional vector spaces.

Example 1 Find an orthogonal basis for the two-dimensional vector space spanned by the vectors $\vec{i} - \vec{j}$ and $\vec{i} + 2\vec{k}$.

Let $\vec{y_1} = \vec{i} - \vec{j}$ and $\vec{y_2} = \vec{i} + 2\vec{k}$. Then a set of vectors $\vec{x_1}$ and $\vec{x_2}$, which constitutes an orthogonal basis for the two-dimensional vector space spanned by $\vec{y_1}$ and $\vec{y_2}$, may be expressed as

$$\vec{x_1} = \vec{i} - \vec{j}$$

and

$$\begin{aligned}\vec{x_2} &= \vec{i} - \vec{j} - \frac{(\vec{i} - \vec{j})\cdot(\vec{i} - \vec{j})}{(\vec{i} - \vec{j})\cdot(\vec{i} + 2\vec{k})}(\vec{i} + 2\vec{k}) \\ &= \vec{i} - \vec{j} - 2(\vec{i} + 2\vec{k}) \\ &= -\vec{i} - \vec{j} - 4\vec{k}.\end{aligned}$$

Note that $\vec{x_1}\cdot\vec{x_2} = 0$.

Example 2 Find an orthonormal basis for the two-dimensional vector space spanned by the vectors given in Example 1.

Now, $\vec{x_1}/|\vec{x_1}|$ and $\vec{x_2}/|\vec{x_2}|$ constitutes an orthonormal basis for the two-dimensional vector space of Example 1. Hence, the vectors

$$\frac{1}{\sqrt{2}}\vec{i} - \frac{1}{\sqrt{2}}\vec{j} \quad \text{and} \quad -\frac{1}{3\sqrt{2}}\vec{i} - \frac{1}{3\sqrt{2}}\vec{j} - \frac{4}{3\sqrt{2}}\vec{k}$$

represent one orthonormal basis.

Example 3 Determine a second orthogonal basis for the vector space of Example 1.

The Gram-Schmidt process may be used again, this time letting $\vec{y_1} = \vec{i} + 2\vec{k}$ and $\vec{y_2} = \vec{i} - \vec{j}$. Then $\vec{x_1} = \vec{i} + 2\vec{k}$ and

$$\begin{aligned}\vec{x_2} &= \vec{i} + 2\vec{k} - \frac{(\vec{i} + 2\vec{k})\cdot(\vec{i} + 2\vec{k})}{(\vec{i} + 2\vec{k})\cdot(\vec{i} - \vec{j})}(\vec{i} - \vec{j}) \\ &= \vec{i} + 2\vec{k} - 5(\vec{i} - \vec{j}) \\ &= -4\vec{i} + 5\vec{j} + 2\vec{k}.\end{aligned}$$

Exercises

1. Determine the values of x for which the vectors $(x - 1)\vec{i} + x\vec{j} + (x + 4)\vec{k}$ and $2\vec{i} + x\vec{j} + \vec{k}$ are orthogonal.
2. Find an orthogonal basis for the two-dimensional vector space spanned by the vectors $\vec{i} + \vec{k}$ and $\vec{i} + \vec{j} + 3\vec{k}$.
3. Find an orthonormal basis for the vector space of Exercise 2.

2-6 The Vector Product

A second type of product of two vectors has for its result a vector, and is called the *vector product*. Consider two vectors $\vec{a}$ and $\vec{b}$ subjected to parallel displacement, if necessary, to bring their initial points into coincidence. Let the smallest angle from $\vec{a}$ to $\vec{b}$ be designated by the symbol $(\vec{a}, \vec{b})$; that is, $0° \leq |(\vec{a}, \vec{b})| \leq 180°$ (Figure 2-18).

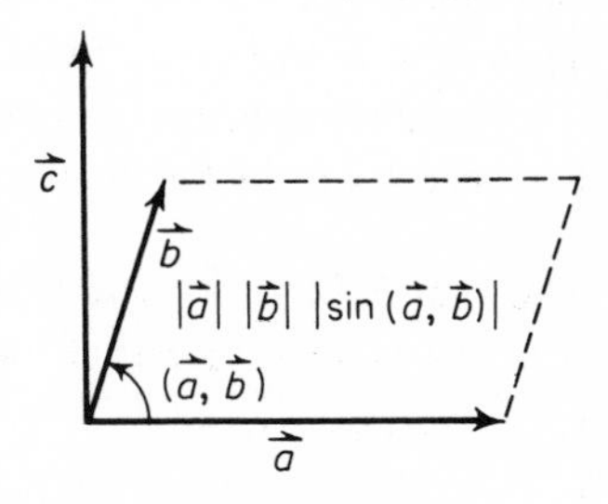

Figure 2-18

Definition 2-2 *The* ***vector, or cross, product*** *of $\vec{a}$ and $\vec{b}$, designated $\vec{a} \times \vec{b}$ and read "$\vec{a}$ cross $\vec{b}$", is defined in general as a third vector $\vec{c}$ such that:*

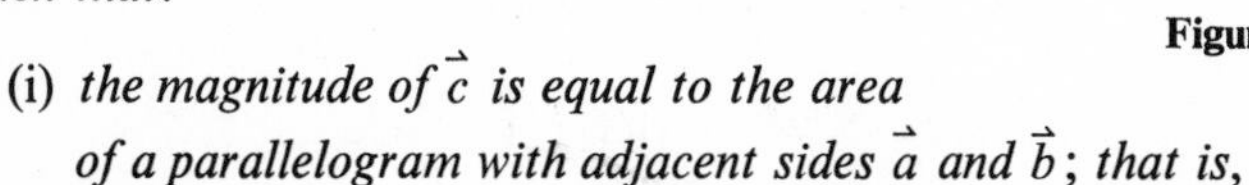

(i) *the magnitude of $\vec{c}$ is equal to the area of a parallelogram with adjacent sides $\vec{a}$ and $\vec{b}$; that is,*

$$|\vec{c}| = |\vec{a}||\vec{b}||\sin(\vec{a}, \vec{b})| \tag{2-25}$$

(ii) *the direction of* $\vec{c}$ *is perpendicular to the plane determined by* $\vec{a}$ *and* $\vec{b}$ *and follows the advances of a right-hand screw when* $\vec{a}$ *is rotated into* $\vec{b}$.

Another name frequently used for the vector product of two vectors is the **outer product.**

From Definition 2-2 it is evident that $|\vec{b} \times \vec{a}| = |\vec{a} \times \vec{b}|$ and the direction of $\vec{b} \times \vec{a}$ is opposite the direction of $\vec{a} \times \vec{b}$. Hence, the vector product of two vectors is generally not commutative and we have:

Theorem 2-8 *The vector product of two vectors is* ***skew-commutative;*** *that is,*

$$\vec{a} \times \vec{b} = -\vec{b} \times \vec{a}. \tag{2-26}$$

Note that when $\vec{a}$ and $\vec{b}$ are parallel vectors the parallelogram of Definition 2-2 may be thought of as a parallelogram with area equal to zero. We sometimes call such a parallelogram a **null parallelogram.**

Theorem 2-9 *If* $\vec{a}$ *and* $\vec{b}$ *are parallel, then* $\vec{a} \times \vec{b} = \vec{0}$.

Theorem 2-10 *For any vector* $\vec{a}$,

$$\vec{a} \times \vec{a} = \vec{0}. \tag{2-27}$$

Notice that if it is given that $\vec{a} \times \vec{b} = \vec{0}$, then $\vec{a}$ and $\vec{b}$ are not necessarily parallel; either $\vec{a}$ and $\vec{b}$ are parallel, or $\vec{a} = \vec{0}$, or $\vec{b} = \vec{0}$.

Theorem 2-11 *If the vector product of two nonzero vectors* $\vec{a}$ *and* $\vec{b}$ *is the zero vector, then the vectors are parallel.*

Since the vector product of two vectors may be the zero vector when neither vector is the zero vector, division of a vector product by a vector, as an inverse process to finding the vector product, cannot be defined. Considering $\vec{a} \times \vec{b} = \vec{a} \times \vec{c}$, then $\vec{b} = \vec{c}$ may or may not be true. For example, consider $\vec{a}$ and $\vec{b}$ to be two nonzero parallel vectors and $\vec{c}$ to be a zero vector. Then $\vec{a} \times \vec{b} = \vec{a} \times \vec{c}$, but $\vec{b} \neq \vec{c}$.

The next theorem will be useful in proving the distributive property of the vector product with respect to the addition of vectors.

Theorem 2-12 *If* $\vec{b}'$ *is the vector component of* $\vec{b}$ *on a line perpendicular to* $\vec{a}$ *in the plane of* $\vec{a}$ *and* $\vec{b}$, *then* $\vec{a} \times \vec{b} = \vec{a} \times \vec{b}'$ (Figure 2-19).

Proof: Now,

$$|\vec{a} \times \vec{b}| = |\vec{a}||\vec{b}||\sin(\vec{a}, \vec{b})|$$

and

$$|\vec{a} \times \vec{b}'| = |\vec{a}||\vec{b}'|.$$

Since

$$|\vec{b}'| = |\vec{b}| \cos [90° - (\vec{a}, \vec{b})]$$
$$= |\vec{b}| |\sin (\vec{a}, \vec{b})|,$$

it follows that $|\vec{a} \times \vec{b}| = |\vec{a} \times \vec{b}'|$. Furthermore, the direction of $\vec{a} \times \vec{b}$ is the same as the direction of $\vec{a} \times \vec{b}'$. Hence, $\vec{a} \times \vec{b} = \vec{a} \times \vec{b}'$.

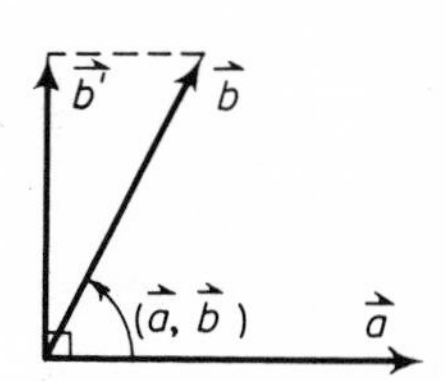

Figure 2-19

Theorem 2-13 *The vector product is distributive with respect to the addition of vectors; that is,*

$$\vec{a} \times (\vec{b} + \vec{c}) = \vec{a} \times \vec{b} + \vec{a} \times \vec{c}. \tag{2-28}$$

Proof: Let $\vec{a}$ be a vector perpendicular to the plane of the paper in the direction of the reader. Let $\vec{b}'$ and $\vec{c}'$ be the vector components of $\vec{b}$ and $\vec{c}$, respectively, in a plane perpendicular to $\vec{a}$. Then $\vec{a} \times \vec{b}'$ and $\vec{a} \times \vec{c}'$ are in the same plane (the plane of the paper) and are perpendicular to $\vec{b}'$ and $\vec{c}'$, respectively, as shown in Figure 2-20. Then

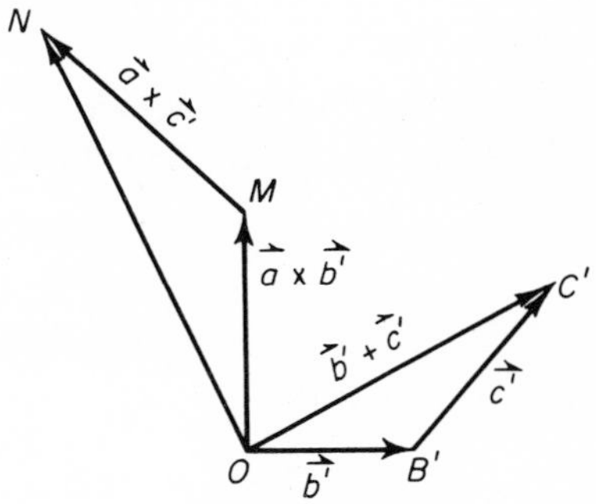

$$\frac{|\vec{a} \times \vec{c}'|}{|\vec{a} \times \vec{b}'|} = \frac{|\vec{a}||\vec{c}'| \sin 90°}{|\vec{a}||\vec{b}'| \sin 90°} = \frac{|\vec{c}'|}{|\vec{b}'|}$$

Figure 2-20

and, since $\angle OMN = \angle OB'C'$, $\triangle OMN \sim \triangle OB'C'$. Hence $\overrightarrow{ON} \perp \overrightarrow{OC}'$, and

$$\frac{|\overrightarrow{ON}|}{|\vec{b}' + \vec{c}'|} = \frac{|\vec{a} \times \vec{b}'|}{|\vec{b}'|};$$

$|\overrightarrow{ON}| = |\vec{a}||\vec{b}' + \vec{c}'| \sin 90°$; that is, $\overrightarrow{ON} = \vec{a} \times (\vec{b}' + \vec{c}')$. From $\triangle OMN$,

$$\overrightarrow{ON} = \overrightarrow{OM} + \overrightarrow{MN} = \vec{a} \times \vec{b}' + \vec{a} \times \vec{c}'.$$

Therefore,

$$\vec{a} \times (\vec{b}' + \vec{c}') = \vec{a} \times \vec{b}' + \vec{a} \times \vec{c}'.$$

Using Theorem 2-12 we may replace $\vec{b}'$ and $\vec{c}'$ by $\vec{b}$ and $\vec{c}$, respectively, so that

$$\vec{a} \times (\vec{b} + \vec{c}) = \vec{a} \times \vec{b} + \vec{a} \times \vec{c}.$$

Theorem 2-14 *A real multiple of the vector product of two vectors is equal to the vector product of one of the vectors and the real multiple of the other; that is,*

$$m(\vec{a} \times \vec{b}) = (m\vec{a}) \times \vec{b} = \vec{a} \times (m\vec{b}). \tag{2-29}$$

Proof: From Definition 2-2 we may write

$$\vec{a} \times \vec{b} = |\vec{a}||\vec{b}||\sin(\vec{a}, \vec{b})|\vec{n},$$

where $\vec{n}$ is a unit vector perpendicular to the plane of $\vec{a}$ and $\vec{b}$, having the direction of the advance of a right-hand screw when the first vector $\vec{a}$ is rotated into the second vector $\vec{b}$. Now, if $m \geq 0$, then

$$\begin{aligned} m(\vec{a} \times \vec{b}) &= m|\vec{a}||\vec{b}||\sin(\vec{a}, \vec{b})|\vec{n} \\ &= |m\vec{a}||\vec{b}||\sin(m\vec{a}, \vec{b})|\vec{n} = (m\vec{a}) \times \vec{b} \\ &= |\vec{a}||m\vec{b}||\sin(\vec{a}, m\vec{b})|\vec{n} = \vec{a} \times (m\vec{b}). \end{aligned}$$

If $m < 0$, then

$$\begin{aligned} m(\vec{a} \times \vec{b}) &= m|\vec{a}||\vec{b}||\sin(\vec{a}, \vec{b})|\vec{n} \\ &= |m\vec{a}||\vec{b}||\sin(m\vec{a}, \vec{b})|(-\vec{n}) = (m\vec{a}) \times \vec{b} \\ &= |\vec{a}||m\vec{b}||\sin(\vec{a}, m\vec{b})|(-\vec{n}) = \vec{a} \times (m\vec{b}). \end{aligned}$$

Consider the unit vectors $\vec{i}$, $\vec{j}$, and $\vec{k}$ for the rectangular cartesian coordinate system. By Definition 2-2

$$\begin{aligned} \vec{i} \times \vec{j} &= -\vec{j} \times \vec{i} = \vec{k}, \\ \vec{j} \times \vec{k} &= -\vec{k} \times \vec{j} = \vec{i}, \\ \vec{k} \times \vec{i} &= -\vec{i} \times \vec{k} = \vec{j}. \end{aligned} \tag{2-30}$$

By Theorem 2-10

$$\begin{aligned} \vec{i} \times \vec{i} &= \vec{0}, \\ \vec{j} \times \vec{j} &= \vec{0}, \\ \vec{k} \times \vec{k} &= \vec{0}. \end{aligned} \tag{2-31}$$

The components of the vector product of two position vectors may now be determined as shown in Theorem 2-15.

Theorem 2-15 *If*

$$\vec{a} = x_1\vec{i} + y_1\vec{j} + z_1\vec{k} \qquad \textit{and} \qquad \vec{b} = x_2\vec{i} + y_2\vec{j} + z_2\vec{k},$$

then

$$\vec{a} \times \vec{b} = (y_1z_2 - y_2z_1)\vec{i} + (z_1x_2 - z_2x_1)\vec{j} + (x_1y_2 - x_2y_1)\vec{k}.$$

Proof:

$$\begin{aligned} \vec{a} \times \vec{b} &= (x_1\vec{i} + y_1\vec{j} + z_1\vec{k}) \times (x_2\vec{i} + y_2\vec{j} + z_2\vec{k}) \\ &= x_1x_2(\vec{i} \times \vec{i}) + x_1y_2(\vec{i} \times \vec{j}) + x_1z_2(\vec{i} \times \vec{k}) \\ &\quad + y_1x_2(\vec{j} \times \vec{i}) + y_1y_2(\vec{j} \times \vec{j}) + y_1z_2(\vec{j} \times \vec{k}) \\ &\quad + z_1x_2(\vec{k} \times \vec{i}) + z_1y_2(\vec{k} \times \vec{j}) + z_1z_2(\vec{k} \times \vec{k}). \end{aligned}$$

By the formulas (2-30) and (2-31),

$$\begin{aligned} \vec{a} \times \vec{b} &= \vec{0} + x_1y_2\vec{k} - x_1z_2\vec{j} - y_1x_2\vec{k} + \vec{0} + y_1z_2\vec{i} + z_1x_2\vec{j} \\ &\quad - z_1y_2\vec{i} + \vec{0}; \end{aligned}$$

$$\vec{a} \times \vec{b} = (y_1z_2 - y_2z_1)\vec{i} + (z_1x_2 - z_2x_1)\vec{j} + (x_1y_2 - x_2y_1)\vec{k}.$$

A **determinant of order n** is a square array of n^2 elements which represents the sum of certain products of these elements. A **determinant of order two** is a square array of the form

$$\begin{vmatrix} a_1 & a_2 \\ b_1 & b_2 \end{vmatrix}$$

whose value is $a_1b_2 - a_2b_1$. A **determinant of order three** is a square array of the form

$$\begin{vmatrix} a_1 & a_2 & a_3 \\ b_1 & b_2 & b_3 \\ c_1 & c_2 & c_3 \end{vmatrix}$$

whose value is

$$a_1\begin{vmatrix} b_2 & b_3 \\ c_2 & c_3 \end{vmatrix} + a_2\begin{vmatrix} b_3 & b_1 \\ c_3 & c_1 \end{vmatrix} + a_3\begin{vmatrix} b_1 & b_2 \\ c_1 & c_2 \end{vmatrix};$$

that is, $a_1b_2c_3 + a_2b_3c_1 + a_3b_1c_2 - a_1b_3c_2 - a_2b_1c_3 - a_3b_2c_1$. It is often convenient to consider the vector product of two position vectors given by Theorem 2-15 in determinant form:

$$\vec{a} \times \vec{b} = \begin{vmatrix} \vec{i} & \vec{j} & \vec{k} \\ x_1 & y_1 & z_1 \\ x_2 & y_2 & z_2 \end{vmatrix}. \tag{2-32}$$

It should be noted that the vector product is a meaningful operation for vectors in three-dimensional space. The vector product of two vectors is defined only for vectors in three-dimensional space.

Example 1 Find $\vec{a} \times \vec{b}$ if $\vec{a} = 3\vec{i} + 2\vec{j} - \vec{k}$ and $\vec{b} = \vec{i} + 4\vec{j} + \vec{k}$.

$$\vec{a} \times \vec{b} = \begin{vmatrix} \vec{i} & \vec{j} & \vec{k} \\ 3 & 2 & -1 \\ 1 & 4 & 1 \end{vmatrix} = 6\vec{i} - 4\vec{j} + 10\vec{k}.$$

Example 2 Find a vector perpendicular to line AB for A: $(0, -1, 3)$ and B: $(2, 0, 4)$, and also perpendicular to line CD for C: $(2, -1, 4)$ and D: $(3, 3, 2)$.

The vectors $\overrightarrow{AB}$ and $\overrightarrow{CD}$ are on lines AB and CD, respectively;

$$\overrightarrow{AB} = 2\vec{i} + \vec{j} + \vec{k};$$
$$\overrightarrow{CD} = \vec{i} + 4\vec{j} - 2\vec{k}.$$

Then

$$\overrightarrow{AB} \times \overrightarrow{CD} = \begin{vmatrix} \vec{i} & \vec{j} & \vec{k} \\ 2 & 1 & 1 \\ 1 & 4 & -2 \end{vmatrix} = -6\vec{i} + 5\vec{j} + 7\vec{k}.$$

Since $\overrightarrow{AB} \times \overrightarrow{CD}$ is perpendicular to $\overrightarrow{AB}$ and $\overrightarrow{CD}$, any real nonzero multiple of $\overrightarrow{AB} \times \overrightarrow{CD}$ is perpendicular to lines AB and CD.

Example 3 Prove that $(\vec{a} - \vec{b}) \times (\vec{a} + \vec{b}) = (2\vec{a}) \times \vec{b}$.

$$\begin{aligned}(\vec{a} - \vec{b}) \times (\vec{a} + \vec{b}) &= (\vec{a} - \vec{b}) \times \vec{a} + (\vec{a} - \vec{b}) \times \vec{b} \\ &= \vec{a} \times (\vec{b} - \vec{a}) + \vec{b} \times (\vec{b} - \vec{a}) \\ &= \vec{a} \times \vec{b} - \vec{a} \times \vec{a} + \vec{b} \times \vec{b} - \vec{b} \times \vec{a} \\ &= \vec{a} \times \vec{b} - \vec{b} \times \vec{a} \\ &= \vec{a} \times \vec{b} + \vec{a} \times \vec{b} \\ &= 2(\vec{a} \times \vec{b}) = (2\vec{a}) \times \vec{b}.\end{aligned}$$

Example 4 Find the area of the parallelogram with adjacent sides associated with $\vec{a} = \vec{i} - \vec{j} + \vec{k}$ and $\vec{b} = 2\vec{j} - 3\vec{k}$.

The magnitude of $\vec{a} \times \vec{b}$ represents the area of the parallelogram with adjacent sides $\vec{a}$ and $\vec{b}$. Since

$$\vec{a} \times \vec{b} = \begin{vmatrix} \vec{i} & \vec{j} & \vec{k} \\ 1 & -1 & 1 \\ 0 & 2 & -3 \end{vmatrix} = \vec{i} + 3\vec{j} + 2\vec{k}$$

and $|\vec{a} \times \vec{b}| = |\vec{i} + 3\vec{j} + 2\vec{k}| = \sqrt{14}$, the area of the parallelogram is $\sqrt{14}$ square units.

Example 5 Prove that $|\vec{a} \times \vec{b}|^2 + |\vec{a} \cdot \vec{b}|^2 = |\vec{a}|^2 |\vec{b}|^2$.

$$\begin{aligned}|\vec{a} \times \vec{b}|^2 + |\vec{a} \cdot \vec{b}|^2 &= |\vec{a}|^2 |\vec{b}|^2 \sin^2 (\vec{a}, \vec{b}) + |\vec{a}|^2 |\vec{b}|^2 \cos^2 (\vec{a}, \vec{b}) \\ &= |\vec{a}|^2 |\vec{b}|^2 [\sin^2 (\vec{a}, \vec{b}) + \cos^2 (\vec{a}, \vec{b})] \\ &= |\vec{a}|^2 |\vec{b}|^2.\end{aligned}$$

Exercises

1. Verify Theorem 2-12 for $\vec{a} = 3\vec{i}$ and $\vec{b} = \vec{i} + 2\vec{j}$.
2. Verify that the vector product is distributive with respect to the addition of vectors using $\vec{a} = 3\vec{i} + \vec{j} - \vec{k}$, $\vec{b} = \vec{i} + 2\vec{j} + \vec{k}$, and $\vec{c} = \vec{i} - \vec{j} + 2\vec{k}$.
3. Show that if $\vec{a} = a_1\vec{i} + a_2\vec{j} + a_3\vec{k}$ and $\vec{b} = b_1\vec{i} + b_2\vec{j} + b_3\vec{k}$, then
$$\vec{a} \times \vec{b} = \begin{vmatrix} a_1 & b_1 & \vec{i} \\ a_2 & b_2 & \vec{j} \\ a_3 & b_3 & \vec{k} \end{vmatrix}.$$
4. Find a vector perpendicular to lines AB and CD where A: (0, 2, 4), B: (3, −1, 2), C: (2, 0, 1), and D: (4, 2, 0).
5. Determine a unit vector perpendicular to $\vec{a} = \vec{i} + \vec{j}$ and $\vec{b} = 3\vec{i} + 2\vec{j} + \vec{k}$.
6. Prove that $(\vec{a} + \vec{b}) \times (\vec{c} + \vec{d}) = (\vec{a} \times \vec{c}) + (\vec{a} \times \vec{d}) + (\vec{b} \times \vec{c}) + (\vec{b} \times \vec{d})$.

7. Find the area of a triangle with adjacent sides $\vec{a} = 3\vec{i} + 2\vec{j}$ and $\vec{b} = 2\vec{j} - 4\vec{k}$.

8. Prove that a necessary and sufficient condition that two vectors be linearly dependent is that their vector product be a null vector.

9. If $\vec{a} + \vec{b} + \vec{c} = \vec{0}$, prove that $\vec{a} \times \vec{b} = \vec{b} \times \vec{c} = \vec{c} \times \vec{a}$.

2-7 Applications of the Vector Product

Many theorems in geometry and trigonometry have simple vector proofs based on the concept of the vector product. In this section we shall illustrate the proofs of several such theorems as well as the usefulness of the concept in physics. Note that a number of the proofs do not involve elements of coordinate geometry.

Example 1 Derive the formula $K = \frac{1}{2}bc \sin A$ for the area of a triangle.

Let A, B, and C be any three vertices of a triangle in space (Figure 2-21). Then the area K of $\triangle ABC$ is equal to one-half the area of a parallelogram with $\overrightarrow{AB}$ and $\overrightarrow{AC}$ forming adjacent edges. Since the area of the parallelogram is the magnitude of $\overrightarrow{AB} \times \overrightarrow{AC}$, it follows that

$$K = \tfrac{1}{2}|\overrightarrow{AB} \times \overrightarrow{AC}|, \tag{2-33}$$

or

$$K = \tfrac{1}{2}|(\overrightarrow{OB} - \overrightarrow{OA}) \times (\overrightarrow{OC} - \overrightarrow{OA})|, \tag{2-34}$$

where $\overrightarrow{OA}$, $\overrightarrow{OB}$, and $\overrightarrow{OC}$ are the position vectors associated with the points A, B, and C, respectively. By Definition 2-2, equation (2-33) may be written as

$$\begin{aligned} K &= \tfrac{1}{2}|\overrightarrow{AB}||\overrightarrow{AC}| \sin (\overrightarrow{AB}, \overrightarrow{AC}) \\ &= \tfrac{1}{2}bc \sin A, \end{aligned}$$

where b and c denote sides AC and AB, respectively.

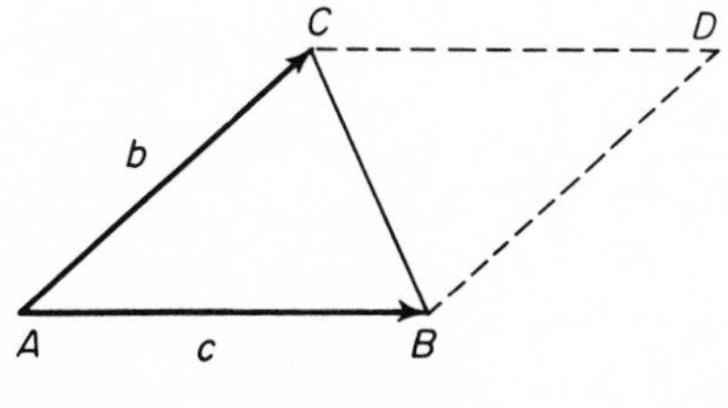

Figure 2-21

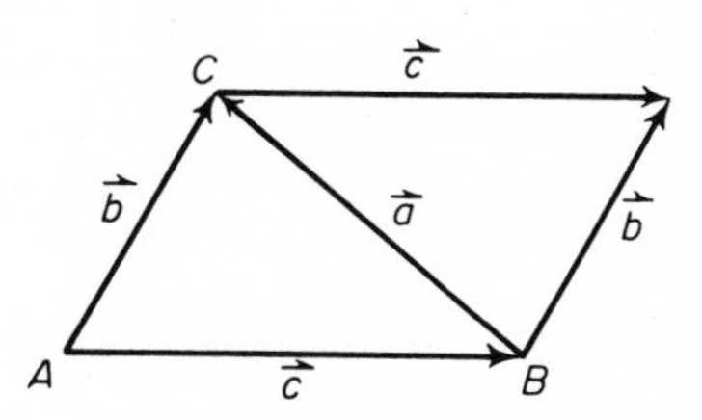

Figure 2-22

Example 2 Find the area of a triangle formed by taking A: $(0, -2, 1)$, B: $(1, -1, -2)$, and C: $(-1, 1, 0)$ as vertices.

Now, $\overrightarrow{AB} = \vec{i} + \vec{j} - 3\vec{k}$; $\overrightarrow{AC} = -\vec{i} + 3\vec{j} - \vec{k}$. Then, as in Example 1,

$$\overrightarrow{AB} \times \overrightarrow{AC} = \begin{vmatrix} \vec{i} & \vec{j} & \vec{k} \\ 1 & 1 & -3 \\ -1 & 3 & -1 \end{vmatrix} = 8\vec{i} + 4\vec{j} + 4\vec{k},$$

and

$$\tfrac{1}{2}|\overrightarrow{AB} \times \overrightarrow{AC}| = \tfrac{1}{2}\sqrt{8^2 + 4^2 + 4^2} = 2\sqrt{6}.$$

Therefore, the area of $\triangle ABC$ is $2\sqrt{6}$ square units.

Example 3 Derive the law of sines.

Let ABC be any triangle. Let $\vec{a}$, $\vec{b}$, and $\vec{c}$ be associated with sides BC, AC, and AB, respectively (Figure 2-22). Now, $\vec{a} = \vec{b} - \vec{c}$. Then

$$\vec{a} \times \vec{a} = \vec{a} \times (\vec{b} - \vec{c}) = \vec{a} \times \vec{b} - \vec{a} \times \vec{c}.$$

Since $\vec{a} \times \vec{a} = \vec{0}$, then $\vec{a} \times \vec{b} - \vec{a} \times \vec{c} = \vec{0}$ and $\vec{a} \times \vec{b} = \vec{a} \times \vec{c}$. Therefore $|\vec{a} \times \vec{b}| = |\vec{a} \times \vec{c}|$, and $|\vec{a}||\vec{b}| \sin C = |\vec{a}||\vec{c}| \sin B$. Then, since $|\vec{a}| \neq 0$,

$$\frac{\sin C}{|\vec{c}|} = \frac{\sin B}{|\vec{b}|}.$$

In a similar manner,

$$\begin{aligned} \vec{b} &= \vec{c} + \vec{a} \\ \vec{b} \times \vec{b} &= \vec{b} \times (\vec{c} + \vec{a}) = \vec{b} \times \vec{c} + \vec{b} \times \vec{a} \\ \vec{0} &= \vec{b} \times \vec{c} + \vec{b} \times \vec{a} \\ \vec{c} \times \vec{b} &= \vec{b} \times \vec{a} \\ |\vec{c} \times \vec{b}| &= |\vec{b} \times \vec{a}| \\ |\vec{c}||\vec{b}| \sin A &= |\vec{b}||\vec{a}| \sin C \\ \frac{\sin A}{|\vec{a}|} &= \frac{\sin C}{|\vec{c}|}. \end{aligned}$$

Hence,

$$\frac{\sin A}{|\vec{a}|} = \frac{\sin B}{|\vec{b}|} = \frac{\sin C}{|\vec{c}|},$$

which is the law of sines.

Example 4 Prove that $\sin(\theta - \phi) = \sin\theta\cos\phi - \cos\theta\sin\phi$.

Let $\vec{a}$ and $\vec{b}$ be unit position vectors on the cartesian coordinate plane making positive angles θ and ϕ with the positive half of the x-axis (Figure 2-23). Consider $\theta \geq \phi$. Then $\vec{a} = \cos\theta\vec{i} + \sin\theta\vec{j}$ and $\vec{b} = \cos\phi\vec{i} + \sin\phi\vec{j}$. By Theorem 2-15,

$$\vec{b} \times \vec{a} = (\sin\theta\cos\phi - \cos\theta\sin\phi)\vec{k}.$$

However, by Definition 2-2 with $|\vec{a}| = |\vec{b}| = 1$ and $\theta \geq \phi$,

$$\vec{b} \times \vec{a} = |\vec{b}||\vec{a}| \sin(\theta - \phi)\vec{k} = \sin(\theta - \phi)\vec{k}.$$

Hence, $\sin(\theta - \phi) = \sin\theta\cos\phi - \cos\theta\sin\phi$.

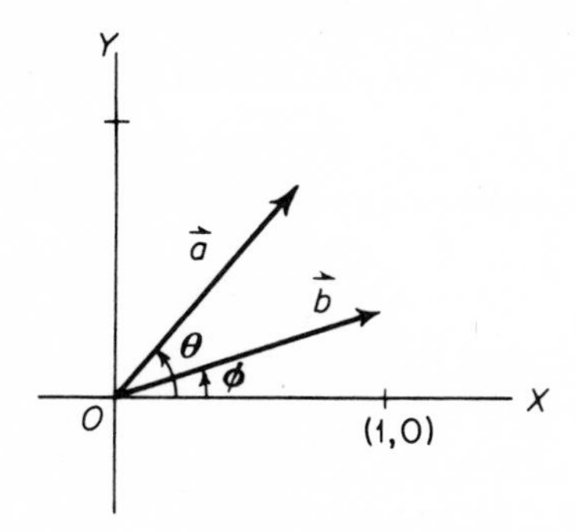

Figure 2-23

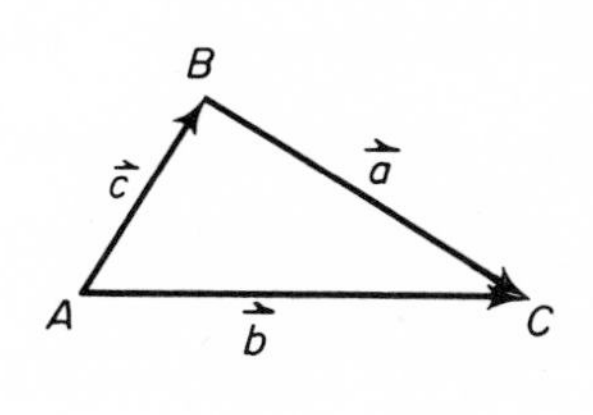

Figure 2-24

Example 5 Derive Hero's formula for the area of a triangle.

Let ABC be any triangle. Let $\vec{a}$, $\vec{b}$, and $\vec{c}$ be associated with sides opposite angles A, B, and C, respectively, as shown in Figure 2-24. The area K of triangle ABC may be expressed by

$$K = \tfrac{1}{2}|\vec{b} \times \vec{c}|.$$

Then

$$2K = |\vec{b} \times \vec{c}|$$
$$4K^2 = |\vec{b} \times \vec{c}|^2.$$

By the results of Example 5 in §2-6,

$$\begin{aligned} 4K^2 &= |\vec{b}|^2|\vec{c}|^2 - (\vec{b}\cdot\vec{c})^2 \\ &= [|\vec{b}||\vec{c}| - (\vec{b}\cdot\vec{c})][|\vec{b}||\vec{c}| + (\vec{b}\cdot\vec{c})] \\ &= [|\vec{b}||\vec{c}| - |\vec{b}||\vec{c}|\cos A][|\vec{b}||\vec{c}| + |\vec{b}||\vec{c}|\cos A]. \end{aligned}$$

By the law of cosines,

$$4K^2 = \left[|\vec{b}||\vec{c}| - \frac{|\vec{b}|^2 + |\vec{c}|^2 - |\vec{a}|^2}{2}\right]\left[|\vec{b}||\vec{c}| + \frac{|\vec{b}|^2 + |\vec{c}|^2 - |\vec{a}|^2}{2}\right]$$

$$16K^2 = [|\vec{a}|^2 - (|\vec{b}| - |\vec{c}|)^2][(|\vec{b}| + |\vec{c}|)^2 - |\vec{a}|^2]$$

$$16K^2 = (|\vec{a}| - |\vec{b}| + |\vec{c}|)(|\vec{a}| + |\vec{b}| - |\vec{c}|)(|\vec{b}| + |\vec{c}| - |\vec{a}|)(|\vec{b}| + |\vec{c}| + |\vec{a}|).$$

If the semiperimeter of $\triangle ABC$ is denoted by S, then

$$S = \frac{|\vec{a}| + |\vec{b}| + |\vec{c}|}{2};$$

$$K^2 = (S - |\vec{b}|)(S - |\vec{c}|)(S - |\vec{a}|)S;$$

$$K = \sqrt{(S - |\vec{b}|)(S - |\vec{c}|)(S - |\vec{a}|)S}.$$

Example 6 Prove that if the diagonals of a given parallelogram are used as sides of a second parallelogram, then the area of the second parallelogram is twice that of the given parallelogram.

Let $\vec{a}$ and $\vec{b}$ be associated with two adjacent sides of a given parallelogram. Then the vectors associated with the diagonals are $\vec{a} + \vec{b}$ and $\vec{a} - \vec{b}$. The area of a parallelogram with the diagonals as sides is expressed by

$$
\begin{aligned}
|(\vec{a} + \vec{b}) \times (\vec{a} - \vec{b})| &= |(\vec{a} + \vec{b}) \times \vec{a} - (\vec{a} + \vec{b}) \times \vec{b}\,| \\
&= |-\vec{a} \times (\vec{a} + \vec{b}) + \vec{b} \times (\vec{a} + \vec{b})| \\
&= |(-\vec{a} \times \vec{a}) + (-\vec{a} \times \vec{b}) + (\vec{b} \times \vec{a}) + (\vec{b} \times \vec{b})| \\
&= |-(\vec{a} \times \vec{b}) + (\vec{b} \times \vec{a})| \\
&= 2\,|(\vec{b} \times \vec{a})|,
\end{aligned}
$$

which is twice the area of the given parallelogram.

Applications of the vector product in physics are varied and numerous. Illustrations of applications to mechanics and light are presented in the next set of examples.

Example 7 Find a vector expression for the velocity of a rigid body rotating with a constant angular velocity about a fixed axis (Figure 2-25).

Consider a rigid body rotating with a constant angular velocity of ω radians per second about a fixed axis l. Let $\vec{\omega}$ be a vector with magnitude ω and direction that of the axis l. Let the origin be chosen on the axis of rotation, and let $\vec{r}$ be a position vector of the point P: (x, y, z) on the path of the rotating body. Now, the velocity $\vec{v}$ of the body at

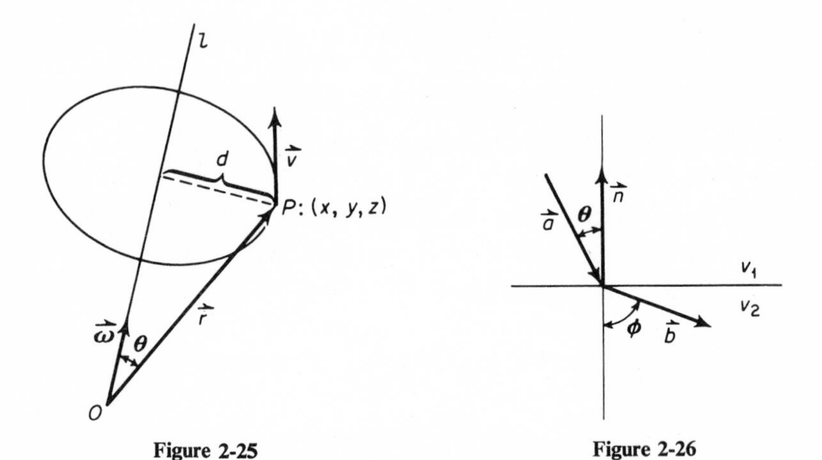

Figure 2-25

Figure 2-26

P is perpendicular to the plane of $\vec{\omega}$ and $\vec{r}$. Let d be the distance between P and l. Then

$$|\vec{v}| = d\omega = |\vec{r}| \sin\theta \, |\vec{\omega}|;$$

that is,

$$\vec{v} = \vec{\omega} \times \vec{r}.$$

Example 8 State Snell's law for the refraction of light in vector form (Figure 2-26).

Consider a ray of light passing from one medium, where the velocity of light is v_1, to a second medium, where the velocity is v_2. Snell's law for refracted light states that the relationship between the angle of incidence θ and the angle of refraction ϕ is expressed by the equation

$$v_1 \sin\phi = v_2 \sin\theta.$$

Let $\vec{n}$, $\vec{a}$, and $\vec{b}$ be unit vectors where $\vec{n}$ is normal to the surface of separation between the media, and $\vec{a}$ and $\vec{b}$ are in the direction of the incident and refracted rays, respectively. Then Snell's law may be stated in vector form as

$$v_2 \vec{a} \times \vec{n} = v_1 \vec{b} \times \vec{n}.$$

Other applications will be considered in subsequent sections of this chapter. In Chapter 3 we shall consider the applications of the vector product to the study of the coordinate geometry of planes and lines in three space.

Exercises

1. Find the area of a triangle whose vertices are A: $(1, 1, -1)$, B: $(2, 1, 0)$, and C: $(0, 1, 0)$.
2. Derive the law of sines by expressing the area of a triangle in vector product form.
3. In the xy-plane, let $\vec{a}$ and $\vec{b}$ be unit vectors making angles θ and $-\phi$ with the positive half of the x-axis. Derive the formula $\sin(\theta + \phi) = \sin\theta\cos\phi + \cos\theta\sin\phi$.
4. A rigid body is rotating with an angular velocity of 3 radians per second about an axis parallel to $2\vec{i} + \vec{j} - 2\vec{k}$ and passing through the point O: $(1, 2, -4)$. Determine the velocity of the rigid body at P: $(2, 1, 1)$.
5. State the law of reflection of light in vector form. Let $\vec{n}$, $\vec{a}$, and $\vec{b}$ be unit vectors where $\vec{n}$ is normal to the surface of reflection, and $\vec{a}$ and $\vec{b}$ are in the direction of the incident and reflected rays, respectively.
6. Give a physical proof of the distributive property of the vector product

by using the hydrostatic principle, that a closed polyhedral surface submerged in a fluid is in equilibrium with respect to the pressures upon its faces. Hint: Use a triangular prism and remember that the pressures normal to the faces are proportional to the areas of the faces.

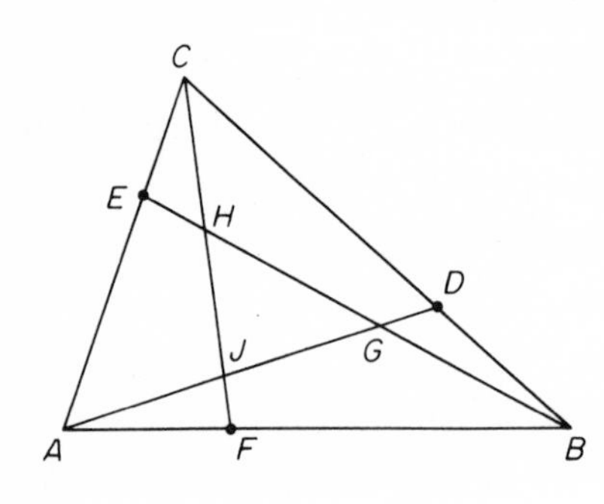

7. Prove that the area of triangle HJG in the given figure is one-seventh the area of triangle ABC. The points D, E, and F divide the line segments BC, CA, and AB, respectively, in the ratio 1 to 2. The points G, H, and J divide the line segments BE, CF, and AD, respectively, in the ratio 3 to 4. The points H, J, and G divide the line segments BE, CF, and AD, respectively, in the ratio 6 to 1.

2-8 The Scalar Triple Product

Let $\vec{a}$, $\vec{b}$, and $\vec{c}$ be any three vectors. The expression

$$\vec{a}\cdot(\vec{b} \times \vec{c}) \tag{2-35}$$

is called the **scalar triple product** of $\vec{a}$, $\vec{b}$, and $\vec{c}$. Note that the scalar triple product is a scalar. For example, $\vec{i}\cdot(\vec{j} \times \vec{k}) = \vec{i}\cdot\vec{i} = 1$; and $\vec{j}\cdot(\vec{j} \times \vec{i}) = \vec{j}\cdot(-\vec{k}) = 0$.

If $\vec{a}$, $\vec{b}$, and $\vec{c}$ are three noncoplanar vectors, then they may be associated with the sides of a parallelepiped as shown in Figure 2-27. There exists a vector perpendicular to the plane of the parallelogram determined by $\vec{b}$ and $\vec{c}$ with magnitude $|\vec{b} \times \vec{c}|$, which is equal to B, the area of the base of the parallelepiped. The magnitude of the projection of $\vec{a}$ on $\vec{b} \times \vec{c}$ is equal to the altitude h of the parallelepiped; that is, $h = |\vec{a}||\cos\theta|$ where θ is the angle between $\vec{a}$ and $\vec{b} \times \vec{c}$. Note that we consider $|\cos\theta|$ instead of simply $\cos\theta$, since the orientation of $\vec{b}$ and $\vec{c}$ relative to one another may be such that $\cos\theta$ would be negative. Hence, the volume V of the parallelepiped is given by the expression

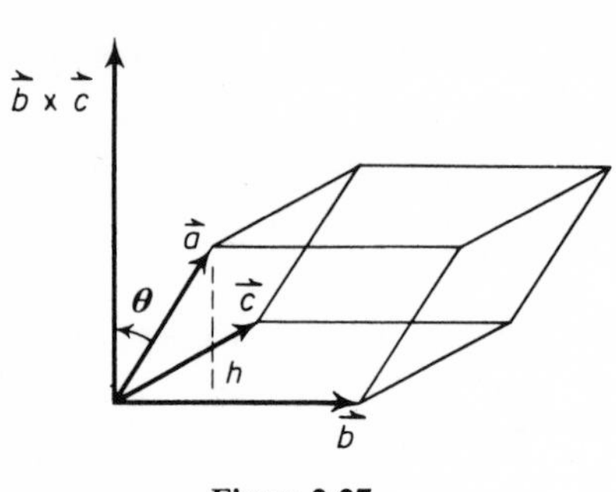

Figure 2-27

$$V = hB = |\vec{a}||\vec{b} \times \vec{c}||\cos\theta|,$$

$$V = |\vec{a}\cdot(\vec{b} \times \vec{c})|; \tag{2-36}$$

that is, *the absolute value of the scalar triple product of any three vectors, $\vec{a}$, $\vec{b}$, and $\vec{c}$, is equal to the volume of a parallelepiped with sides $\vec{a}$, $\vec{b}$, and $\vec{c}$ having the same initial point.*

If $\vec{a}$, $\vec{b}$, and $\vec{c}$ are position vectors, where $\vec{a} = a_1\vec{i} + a_2\vec{j} + a_3\vec{k}$, $\vec{b} = b_1\vec{i} + b_2\vec{j} + b_3\vec{k}$, and $\vec{c} = c_1\vec{i} + c_2\vec{j} + c_3\vec{k}$, *then, since*

$$\vec{b} \times \vec{c} = (b_2c_3 - b_3c_2)\vec{i} + (b_3c_1 - b_1c_3)\vec{j} + (b_1c_2 - b_2c_1)\vec{k},$$

it follows that

$$\vec{a}\cdot(\vec{b} \times \vec{c}) = a_1(b_2c_3 - b_3c_2) + a_2(b_3c_1 - b_1c_3) + a_3(b_1c_2 - b_2c_1); \qquad (2\text{-}37)$$

that is,

$$\vec{a}\cdot(\vec{b} \times \vec{c}) = \begin{vmatrix} a_1 & a_2 & a_3 \\ b_1 & b_2 & b_3 \\ c_1 & c_2 & c_3 \end{vmatrix}. \qquad (2\text{-}38)$$

From elementary theorems on determinants it can be shown that the interchange of two rows produces a change of sign of the value of the determinant. An even number of such interchanges leaves the value unchanged. Thus, the scalar triple product is not changed by a cyclical permutation of the vectors; that is,

$$\vec{a}\cdot(\vec{b} \times \vec{c}) = \vec{b}\cdot(\vec{c} \times \vec{a}) = \vec{c}\cdot(\vec{a} \times \vec{b}). \qquad (2\text{-}39)$$

Since the scalar product of two vectors is commutative,

$$\vec{c}\cdot(\vec{a} \times \vec{b}) = (\vec{a} \times \vec{b})\cdot\vec{c}.$$

Using equation (2-39),

$$\vec{a}\cdot(\vec{b} \times \vec{c}) = (\vec{a} \times \vec{b})\cdot\vec{c}. \qquad (2\text{-}40)$$

Therefore, in the scalar triple product the operations of scalar and vector products may be interchanged without changing the value of the result. For this reason $\vec{a}\cdot(\vec{b} \times \vec{c})$ is sometimes written without the parenthesis and sometimes without any multiplication signs since only one interpretation is possible; that is,

$$\vec{a}\cdot(\vec{b} \times \vec{c}) = \vec{a}\cdot\vec{b} \times \vec{c} = (\vec{a}\vec{b}\vec{c}). \qquad (2\text{-}41)$$

It should be further noted that

$$(\vec{a}\vec{b}\vec{c}) = -(\vec{b}\vec{a}\vec{c}) = -(\vec{c}\vec{b}\vec{a}) = -(\vec{a}\vec{c}\vec{b}). \qquad (2\text{-}42)$$

The verification of these results are left to the reader as an exercise.

If the three vectors $\vec{a}, \vec{b}, \vec{c}$ are coplanar, then the parallelepiped is a **degenerate**, or **null, parallelepiped;** that is, a parallelepiped whose volume is zero. Hence $(\vec{a}\vec{b}\vec{c}) = 0$. In particular, if two of the three vectors are parallel, the scalar triple product vanishes. The proof is left to the reader as an exercise.

Example 1 Find the volume of the parallelepiped whose edges are $\vec{a}$, $\vec{b}$, and $\vec{c}$, where $\vec{a} = 3\vec{i} + 2\vec{k}$, $\vec{b} = \vec{i} + 2\vec{j} + \vec{k}$, and $\vec{c} = -\vec{j} + 4\vec{k}$.

The volume of the parallelepiped is given by $|\vec{a}\cdot(\vec{b}\times\vec{c})|$.

$$\vec{a}\cdot(\vec{b}\times\vec{c}) = \begin{vmatrix} 3 & 0 & 2 \\ 1 & 2 & 1 \\ 0 & -1 & 4 \end{vmatrix},$$

$$= 3\begin{vmatrix} 2 & 1 \\ -1 & 4 \end{vmatrix} + 2\begin{vmatrix} 1 & 2 \\ 0 & -1 \end{vmatrix},$$

$$= 27 - 2 = 25.$$

The volume of the parallelepiped is 25 cubic units.

Example 2 Find a formula for the volume of a tetrahedron in terms of the coordinates of its vertices.

Let A: (x_1, y_1, z_1), B: (x_2, y_2, z_2), C: (x_3, y_3, z_3), and D: (x_4, y_4, z_4) be the four vertices of a tetrahedron. Then

$$\vec{AB} = (x_2 - x_1)\vec{i} + (y_2 - y_1)\vec{j} + (z_2 - z_1)\vec{k},$$
$$\vec{AC} = (x_3 - x_1)\vec{i} + (y_3 - y_1)\vec{j} + (z_3 - z_1)\vec{k},$$
$$\vec{AD} = (x_4 - x_1)\vec{i} + (y_4 - y_1)\vec{j} + (z_4 - z_1)\vec{k}.$$

The volume of a parallelepiped whose edges are $\vec{AB}$, $\vec{AC}$, and $\vec{AD}$ is given by the expression

$$|\vec{AB}\cdot(\vec{AC}\times\vec{AD})| = \begin{vmatrix} x_2 - x_1 & y_2 - y_1 & z_2 - z_1 \\ x_3 - x_1 & y_3 - y_1 & z_3 - z_1 \\ x_4 - x_1 & y_4 - y_1 & z_4 - z_1 \end{vmatrix}.$$

The volume of a tetrahedron is one-third the product of the area of its base and its altitude. Since the area of the base of the tetrahedron is one-half the area of the base of the parallelepiped, it follows that the volume V of the tetrahedron is one-sixth the volume of the parallelepiped. Hence,

$$V = \tfrac{1}{6}|\vec{AB}\cdot(\vec{AC}\times\vec{AD})|; \qquad (2\text{-}43)$$

that is,

$$V = \pm\tfrac{1}{6}\begin{vmatrix} x_2 - x_1 & y_2 - y_1 & z_2 - z_1 \\ x_3 - x_1 & y_3 - y_1 & z_3 - z_1 \\ x_4 - x_1 & y_4 - y_1 & z_4 - z_1 \end{vmatrix},$$

where the appropriate sign is chosen such that V is non-negative.

Example 3 Prove the distributive law for the vector product by letting $\vec{n} = \vec{a}\times(\vec{b}+\vec{c}) - \vec{a}\times\vec{b} - \vec{a}\times\vec{c}$, and finding $\vec{m}\cdot\vec{n}$ where $\vec{m}$ is an arbitrary nonzero vector.

Now,

$$\begin{aligned}
\vec{m}\cdot\vec{n} &= \vec{m}\cdot[\vec{a}\times(\vec{b}+\vec{c})-\vec{a}\times\vec{b}-\vec{a}\times\vec{c}] \\
&= \vec{m}\cdot[\vec{a}\times(\vec{b}+\vec{c})]-\vec{m}\cdot[\vec{a}\times\vec{b}]-\vec{m}\cdot[\vec{a}\times\vec{c}] \\
&= [(\vec{m}\times\vec{a})\cdot(\vec{b}+\vec{c})]-[(\vec{m}\times\vec{a})\cdot\vec{b}]-[(\vec{m}\times\vec{a})\cdot\vec{c}] \\
&= [(\vec{m}\times\vec{a})\cdot\vec{b}]+[(\vec{m}\times\vec{a})\cdot\vec{c}]-[(\vec{m}\times\vec{a})\cdot\vec{b}]-[(\vec{m}\times\vec{a})\cdot\vec{c}] \\
&= 0.
\end{aligned}$$

Since $\vec{m}$ is an arbitrary nonzero vector, $\vec{m}$ need not be perpendicular to $\vec{n}$. Hence $\vec{n}$ must be a null vector, and $\vec{a}\times(\vec{b}+\vec{c})=\vec{a}\times\vec{b}+\vec{a}\times\vec{c}$.

Example 4 Determine a condition under which four distinct points are coplanar (Figure 2-28).

Let $\vec{a}$, $\vec{b}$, $\vec{c}$, and $\vec{d}$ be position vectors associated with four distinct coplanar points A, B, C, and D, respectively. Then $\overrightarrow{AC}\times\overrightarrow{AD}$ is a vector perpendicular to the plane of A, B, C, and D, and therefore is perpendicular to $\overrightarrow{AB}$. Hence $\overrightarrow{AB}\cdot(\overrightarrow{AC}\times\overrightarrow{AD})=0$, and

$$(\vec{b}-\vec{a})\cdot(\vec{c}-\vec{a})\times(\vec{d}-\vec{a})=0 \tag{2-44}$$

is a necessary condition for four points A, B, C, and D to be coplanar. It can also be shown to be a sufficient condition for four distinct points to be coplanar.

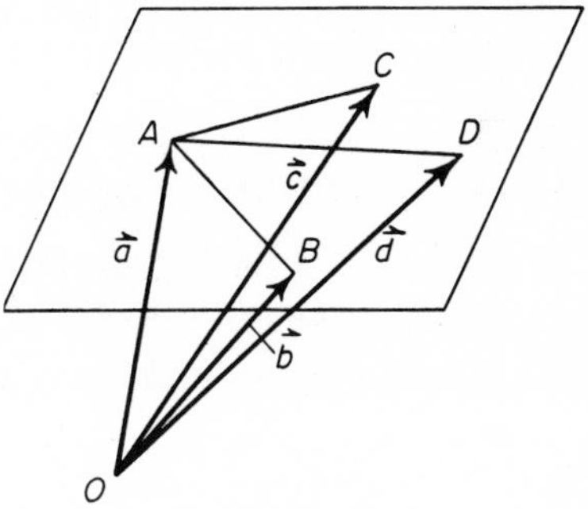

Figure 2-28

The condition that four distinct points be coplanar may also be expressed by Theorem 1-5 in the alternate form

$$\overrightarrow{AB}=x\overrightarrow{AC}+y\overrightarrow{AD}.$$

Then

$$\vec{b}-\vec{a}=x(\vec{c}-\vec{a})+y(\vec{d}-\vec{a}),$$

$$(x+y-1)\vec{a}+\vec{b}-x\vec{c}-y\vec{d}=\vec{0};$$

that is, scalars k_1, k_2, k_3, and k_4, not all zero, must exist such that

$$k_1\vec{a}+k_2\vec{b}+k_3\vec{c}+k_4\vec{d}=\vec{0}, \tag{2-45}$$

where

$$k_1+k_2+k_3+k_4=0.$$

Exercises

1. Find: (a) $\vec{j}\cdot\vec{k}\times\vec{i}$; (b) $\vec{k}\cdot\vec{j}\times\vec{i}$; (c) $\vec{i}\cdot\vec{j}\times\vec{i}$.
2. Verify that $(\vec{a}\vec{b}\vec{c}) = -(\vec{b}\vec{a}\vec{c}) = -(\vec{c}\vec{b}\vec{a}) = -(\vec{a}\vec{c}\vec{b})$.
3. Find the volume of the parallelepiped whose edges are $\vec{a} = \vec{i} + \vec{k}$, $\vec{b} = \vec{i} + \vec{j}$, and $\vec{c} = \vec{j} + \vec{k}$.
4. Find the volume of the tetrahedron whose vertices are A: (1, 0, 2), B: (4, 3, 0), C: (2, 0, 1), and D: (3, 4, 0).
5. Find the volume of the tetrahedron whose faces lie in the coordinate planes and the plane $2x + y + 3z - 6 = 0$.
6. Describe geometrically when $\vec{a}\cdot(\vec{b}\times\vec{c})$ is (a) positive; (b) negative.
7. Verify (2-40) for $\vec{a} = 2\vec{i} + 3\vec{j} - 4\vec{k}$, $\vec{b} = \vec{i} - \vec{j} + \vec{k}$, and $\vec{c} = \vec{i} + \vec{j} + 2\vec{k}$.
8. Prove that (2-44) is a sufficient condition for the terminal points of $\vec{a}$, $\vec{b}$, $\vec{c}$, and $\vec{d}$ to be coplanar.
9. Determine if the four points A: (1, 2, 3), B: (−1, 0, 2), C: (4, 1, 2), and D: (4, 3, 5) are coplanar.
10. Determine if the position vectors $\vec{a} = \vec{i} + \vec{j} + 2\vec{k}$, $\vec{b} = 2\vec{i} - 3\vec{j} + \vec{k}$, and $\vec{c} = \vec{i} - 4\vec{j} - \vec{k}$ are coplanar.

2-9 The Vector Triple Product

In this section we shall be concerned with another triple product involving vectors, which finds wide application in geometry, trigonometry, and physics. The expression

$$\vec{a}\times(\vec{b}\times\vec{c}) \tag{2-46}$$

is called a **vector triple product** of $\vec{a}$, $\vec{b}$, and $\vec{c}$. Note that the result is a vector. For example, $\vec{i}\times(\vec{j}\times\vec{k}) = \vec{i}\times\vec{i} = \vec{0}$; and $\vec{j}\times(\vec{j}\times\vec{i}) = \vec{j}\times(-\vec{k}) = -\vec{i}$. Furthermore, note that the vector product is not associative. That is,

$$\vec{a}\times(\vec{b}\times\vec{c}) \neq (\vec{a}\times\vec{b})\times\vec{c}.$$

For example, $(\vec{i}\times\vec{i})\times\vec{j} = \vec{0}$, while $\vec{i}\times(\vec{i}\times\vec{j}) = -\vec{j}$.

Since $\vec{b}\times\vec{c}$ is perpendicular to the plane determined by $\vec{b}$ and $\vec{c}$, and $\vec{a}\times(\vec{b}\times\vec{c})$ is perpendicular to $\vec{a}$ and $\vec{b}\times\vec{c}$, then $\vec{a}\times(\vec{b}\times\vec{c})$ must be a vector on the plane determined by $\vec{b}$ and $\vec{c}$. Hence, $\vec{a}\times(\vec{b}\times\vec{c})$ is a linear function of $\vec{b}$ and $\vec{c}$.

Theorem 2-16

$$\vec{a}\times(\vec{b}\times\vec{c}) = (\vec{a}\cdot\vec{c})\vec{b} - (\vec{a}\cdot\vec{b})\vec{c}. \tag{2-47}$$

Proof: Let $\vec{a} \times (\vec{b} \times \vec{c}) = x\vec{b} + y\vec{c}$. Since $\vec{a} \times (\vec{b} \times \vec{c})$ is perpendicular to $\vec{a}$, then

$$\vec{a} \cdot [\vec{a} \times (\vec{b} \times \vec{c})] = 0,$$

and

$$x(\vec{a} \cdot \vec{b}) + y(\vec{a} \cdot \vec{c}) = 0.$$

Now, x and y must necessarily be of the form of multiples of $\vec{a} \cdot \vec{c}$ and $\vec{a} \cdot \vec{b}$, respectively; that is, $x = m(\vec{a} \cdot \vec{c})$, and $y = -m(\vec{a} \cdot \vec{b})$, where m is an arbitrary scalar. Therefore

$$\vec{a} \times (\vec{b} \times \vec{c}) = m[(\vec{a} \cdot \vec{c})\vec{b} - (\vec{a} \cdot \vec{b})\vec{c}]. \tag{2-48}$$

Since corresponding components of this vector equation must be equal, we need only look at the coefficients of $\vec{i}$, $\vec{j}$, or $\vec{k}$ to determine m. Let $\vec{a} = a_1\vec{i} + a_2\vec{j} + a_3\vec{k}$, $\vec{b} = b_1\vec{i} + b_2\vec{j} + b_3\vec{k}$, and $\vec{c} = c_1\vec{i} + c_2\vec{j} + c_3\vec{k}$. Then, equating the coefficients of $\vec{i}$ after substituting for $\vec{a}$, $\vec{b}$, and $\vec{c}$ in (2-48), we have

$$\begin{aligned} a_2(b_1c_2 - b_2c_1) - a_3(b_3c_1 - b_1c_3) &= mb_1(a_1c_1 + a_2c_2 + a_3c_3) \\ &\quad - mc_1(a_1b_1 + a_2b_2 + a_3b_3) \\ &= m[a_2(b_1c_2 - b_2c_1) - a_3(b_3c_1 - b_1c_3)]. \end{aligned}$$

Hence, $m = 1$, and $\vec{a} \times (\vec{b} \times \vec{c}) = (\vec{a} \cdot \vec{c})\vec{b} - (\vec{a} \cdot \vec{b})\vec{c}$.

In a similar manner we may show that

$$(\vec{a} \times \vec{b}) \times \vec{c} = (\vec{a} \cdot \vec{c})\vec{b} - (\vec{b} \cdot \vec{c})\vec{a}. \tag{2-49}$$

Exercises

1. Find: **(a)** $\vec{i} \times (\vec{j} \times \vec{k})$; **(b)** $\vec{i} \times (\vec{j} \times \vec{i})$; **(c)** $(\vec{i} \times \vec{j}) \times \vec{i}$.
2. Verify (2-47) for $\vec{a} = 3\vec{i} - 2\vec{j} + \vec{k}$, $\vec{b} = 2\vec{i} - 2\vec{k}$, and $\vec{c} = \vec{i} + 3\vec{j}$.
3. Prove the identity: $\vec{a} \times (\vec{b} \times \vec{c}) + \vec{b} \times (\vec{c} \times \vec{a}) + \vec{c} \times (\vec{a} \times \vec{b}) = \vec{0}$.
4. Prove that if $\vec{a}$, $\vec{b}$, $\vec{c}$, and $\vec{d}$ are coplanar, then $(\vec{a} \times \vec{b}) \times (\vec{c} \times \vec{d}) = \vec{0}$.

2-10 Quadruple Products

The concepts of the scalar triple product and the vector triple product make it possible to evaluate combinations of multiple vector and scalar products. As an illustration of the process, we shall in this section present an example of a scalar product of four vectors and an example of a vector product of four vectors. These illustrations will then be applied to the subject of spherical trigonometry.

Consider the scalar product $(\vec{a} \times \vec{b}) \cdot (\vec{c} \times \vec{d})$ of the four vectors $\vec{a}$, $\vec{b}$, $\vec{c}$ and $\vec{d}$. Now,

$$\begin{aligned}(\vec{a} \times \vec{b})\cdot(\vec{c} \times \vec{d}) &= \vec{a}\cdot[\vec{b} \times (\vec{c} \times \vec{d})] \\ &= \vec{a}\cdot[(\vec{b}\cdot\vec{d})\vec{c} - (\vec{b}\cdot\vec{c})\vec{d}] \\ &= (\vec{a}\cdot\vec{c})(\vec{b}\cdot\vec{d}) - (\vec{a}\cdot\vec{d})(\vec{b}\cdot\vec{c});\end{aligned}$$

$$(\vec{a} \times \vec{b})\cdot(\vec{c} \times \vec{d}) = \begin{vmatrix} \vec{a}\cdot\vec{c} & \vec{a}\cdot\vec{d} \\ \vec{b}\cdot\vec{c} & \vec{b}\cdot\vec{d} \end{vmatrix}. \qquad (2\text{-}50)$$

Example 1 Derive the cosine law of spherical trigonometry.

Let ABC be any spherical triangle on a unit sphere with sides a, b, and c (arcs of great circles). Then, since the sphere is a unit sphere, the lengths of sides a, b, and c are equal to the radian measures of angle BOC, COA, and AOB, respectively (Figure 2-29). Now,

$$(\overrightarrow{OA} \times \overrightarrow{OB})\cdot(\overrightarrow{OA} \times \overrightarrow{OC}) = (\overrightarrow{OA}\cdot\overrightarrow{OA})(\overrightarrow{OB}\cdot\overrightarrow{OC}) - (\overrightarrow{OA}\cdot\overrightarrow{OC})(\overrightarrow{OB}\cdot\overrightarrow{OA})$$

where $|\overrightarrow{OA} \times \overrightarrow{OB}| = \sin c$, $|\overrightarrow{OA} \times \overrightarrow{OC}| = \sin b$, $\overrightarrow{OB}\cdot\overrightarrow{OC} = \cos a$, $\overrightarrow{OA}\cdot\overrightarrow{OC} = \cos b$, and $\overrightarrow{OB}\cdot\overrightarrow{OA} = \cos c$. The angle between $(\overrightarrow{OA} \times \overrightarrow{OB})$ and $(\overrightarrow{OA} \times \overrightarrow{OC})$ has the same measure as the dihedral angle between the planes OAB and OAC; that is, the angle A of the spherical triangle ABC. Therefore,

$$\sin c \sin b \cos A = \cos a - \cos b \cos c.$$

By a cyclic permutation of the elements, two similar formulas may be obtained:

$$\sin a \sin c \cos B = \cos b - \cos c \cos a;$$

$$\sin b \sin a \cos C = \cos c - \cos a \cos b.$$

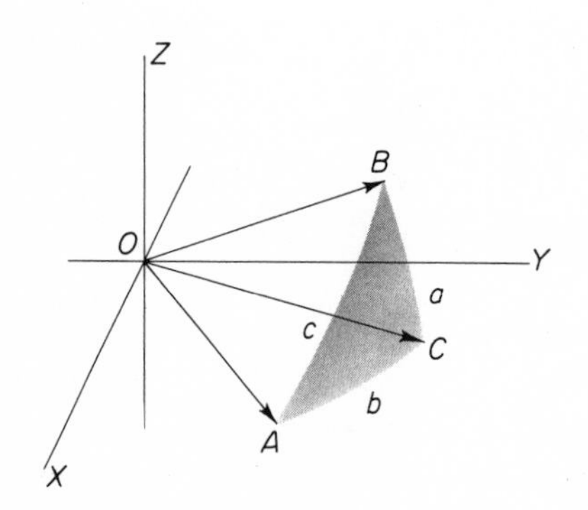

Figure 2-29

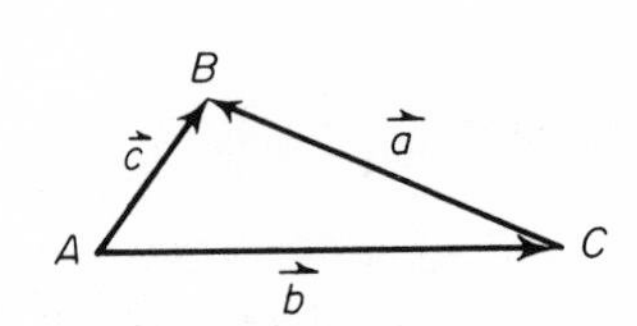

Figure 2-30

Example 2 Use the quadruple product

$$(\vec{b} \times \vec{c})\cdot(\vec{b} \times \vec{c}) = (\vec{c} \times \vec{a})\cdot(\vec{c} \times \vec{a})$$

to obtain a formula for the area of a triangle.

Let $\vec{a}$, $\vec{b}$, and $\vec{c}$ be associated with the sides of a triangle (Figure 2-30). Then the area K may be expressed as $\frac{1}{2}|\vec{b} \times \vec{c}|$, as $\frac{1}{2}|\vec{c} \times \vec{a}|$, and as $\frac{1}{2}|\vec{b} \times \vec{a}|$. Since $|\vec{b} \times \vec{c}|^2 = (\vec{b} \times \vec{c})\cdot(\vec{b} \times \vec{c})$ and $|\vec{c} \times \vec{a}|^2 = (\vec{c} \times \vec{a})\cdot(\vec{c} \times \vec{a})$, then $(\vec{b} \times \vec{c})\cdot(\vec{b} \times \vec{c}) = (\vec{c} \times \vec{a})\cdot(\vec{c} \times \vec{a})$,

$$2K(|\vec{b}||\vec{c}|\sin A) = (|\vec{c}||\vec{a}|\sin B)(|\vec{b}||\vec{a}|\sin C),$$

$$K = \frac{|\vec{a}|^2 \sin B \sin C}{2 \sin A}.$$

Consider the vector product $(\vec{a} \times \vec{b}) \times (\vec{c} \times \vec{d})$ of the four vectors $\vec{a}$, $\vec{b}$, $\vec{c}$, and $\vec{d}$. The resulting vector is perpendicular to $\vec{a} \times \vec{b}$ and $\vec{c} \times \vec{d}$ and therefore lies both on the plane determined by $\vec{a}$ and $\vec{b}$, and the plane determined by $\vec{c}$ and $\vec{d}$ (See §2-9). Hence, $(\vec{a} \times \vec{b}) \times (\vec{c} \times \vec{d})$ may be expressed both as a linear function of $\vec{a}$ and $\vec{b}$ and as a linear function of $\vec{c}$ and $\vec{d}$. Now considering $(\vec{a} \times \vec{b}) \times (\vec{c} \times \vec{d})$ as a vector triple product of $\vec{a}$, $\vec{b}$, and $\vec{c} \times \vec{d}$, we have, by (2-49),

$$(\vec{a} \times \vec{b}) \times (\vec{c} \times \vec{d}) = (\vec{a}\vec{c}\vec{d})\vec{b} - (\vec{b}\vec{c}\vec{d})\vec{a}. \tag{2-51}$$

In a similar manner, considering $(\vec{a} \times \vec{b}) \times (\vec{c} \times \vec{d})$ as a vector triple product of $\vec{a} \times \vec{b}$, $\vec{c}$, and $\vec{d}$, we have

$$(\vec{a} \times \vec{b}) \times (\vec{c} \times \vec{d}) = (\vec{a}\vec{b}\vec{d})\vec{c} - (\vec{a}\vec{b}\vec{c})\vec{d}. \tag{2-52}$$

Hence, by equations (2-51) and (2-52),

$$(\vec{b}\vec{c}\vec{d})\vec{a} - (\vec{a}\vec{c}\vec{d})\vec{b} + (\vec{a}\vec{b}\vec{d})\vec{c} - (\vec{a}\vec{b}\vec{c})\vec{d} = \vec{0}.$$

Example 3 Show that

$$(\vec{e} \times \vec{f}) \times (\vec{f} \times \vec{g}) = (\vec{f}\vec{g}\vec{e})\vec{f}. \tag{2-53}$$

By equation (2-52), with $\vec{e} = \vec{a}$, $\vec{f} = \vec{b} = \vec{c}$, and $\vec{g} = \vec{d}$,

$$\begin{aligned}(\vec{e} \times \vec{f}) \times (\vec{f} \times \vec{g}) &= (\vec{e}\vec{f}\vec{g})\vec{f} - (\vec{e}\vec{f}\vec{f})\vec{g} \\ &= (\vec{e}\vec{f}\vec{g})\vec{f} \\ &= (\vec{f}\vec{g}\vec{e})\vec{f}.\end{aligned}$$

Example 4 Derive the sine law of spherical trigonometry.

Let ABC be any spherical triangle on a unit sphere as in Example 1 and Figure 2-29. By equation (2-52),

$$(\overrightarrow{OA} \times \overrightarrow{OB}) \times (\overrightarrow{OA} \times \overrightarrow{OC}) = (\overrightarrow{OA}\cdot\overrightarrow{OB} \times \overrightarrow{OC})\overrightarrow{OA}$$

and

$$|(\overrightarrow{OA} \times \overrightarrow{OB}) \times (\overrightarrow{OA} \times \overrightarrow{OC})| = |\overrightarrow{OA}\cdot\overrightarrow{OB} \times \overrightarrow{OC}|.$$

Now $|\overrightarrow{OA} \times \overrightarrow{OB}| = \sin c$, $|\overrightarrow{OA} \times \overrightarrow{OC}| = \sin b$, and the angle between $(\overrightarrow{OA} \times \overrightarrow{OB})$ and $(\overrightarrow{OA} \times \overrightarrow{OC})$ is angle A of the spherical triangle ABC. Therefore,

$$\sin c \sin b \sin A = |\overrightarrow{OA}\cdot\overrightarrow{OB} \times \overrightarrow{OC}|.$$

By equation (2-52),

$$(\overrightarrow{OB} \times \overrightarrow{OC}) \times (\overrightarrow{OB} \times \overrightarrow{OA}) = (\overrightarrow{OB} \cdot \overrightarrow{OC} \times \overrightarrow{OA})\overrightarrow{OB}$$

and

$$|(\overrightarrow{OB} \times \overrightarrow{OC}) \times (\overrightarrow{OB} \times \overrightarrow{OA})| = |\overrightarrow{OB} \cdot \overrightarrow{OC} \times \overrightarrow{OA}| = |\overrightarrow{OA} \cdot \overrightarrow{OB} \times \overrightarrow{OC}|.$$

Now $|\overrightarrow{OB} \times \overrightarrow{OC}| = \sin a$, $|\overrightarrow{OB} \times \overrightarrow{OA}| = \sin c$, and the angle between $(\overrightarrow{OB} \times \overrightarrow{OC})$ and $(\overrightarrow{OB} \times \overrightarrow{OA})$ is angle B of the spherical triangle ABC. Therefore,

$$\sin a \sin c \sin B = |\overrightarrow{OA} \cdot \overrightarrow{OB} \times \overrightarrow{OC}|.$$

Hence

$$\sin c \sin b \sin A = \sin a \sin c \sin B;$$

that is,

$$\frac{\sin A}{\sin a} = \frac{\sin B}{\sin b}.$$

By a cyclic permutation of the elements, it follows that

$$\frac{\sin B}{\sin b} = \frac{\sin C}{\sin c},$$

and thus that

$$\frac{\sin A}{\sin a} = \frac{\sin B}{\sin b} = \frac{\sin C}{\sin c}.$$

Exercises

In Exercises 1 through 3 prove the given identities. Use the definition $\vec{a}^2 = \vec{a} \cdot \vec{a}$.

1. $(\vec{a} \times \vec{b}) \cdot (\vec{b} \times \vec{c}) \times (\vec{c} \times \vec{a}) = (\vec{a}\vec{b}\vec{c})^2$.
2. $(\vec{a} \times \vec{b}) \times (\vec{a} \times \vec{c}) = (\vec{a}\vec{b}\vec{c})\vec{a}$
3. $(\vec{a} \times \vec{b}) \cdot (\vec{c} \times \vec{d}) \times (\vec{e} \times \vec{f}) = (\vec{a}\vec{b}\vec{d})(\vec{c}\vec{e}\vec{f}) - (\vec{a}\vec{b}\vec{c})(\vec{d}\vec{e}\vec{f})$.
4. Prove that if $\vec{a}$ is perpendicular to $\vec{b}$ and $\vec{c}$, then $(\vec{a}\vec{b}\vec{c})^2 = \vec{a}^2(\vec{b} \times \vec{c})^2$.
5. Verify (2-50) for $\vec{a} = 3\vec{i} - 2\vec{j} + \vec{k}$, $\vec{b} = 2\vec{i} - 2\vec{k}$, $\vec{c} = \vec{i} + 3\vec{j}$, and $\vec{d} = \vec{i} + \vec{j} - \vec{k}$.

2-11 Quaternions

The forerunner of vector algebra was the subject of quaternions, the major contribution to mathematics of the Irish physicist and mathematician, William Rowan Hamilton. Hamilton was mainly interested in developing an algebraic system which could describe rotations in space. For example, the unit vector $\vec{i}$ in the vector product $\vec{i} \times \vec{j}$ may be considered as an operator which rotates $\vec{j}$ through an angle of 90° in the plane perpendicular to $\vec{i}$ so as to coincide with $\vec{k}$. The story goes that after years of study on the problem, the key concept of the subject became clear to Hamilton one evening in 1843 while walking along the Royal Canal in Dublin. He immediately engraved the fundamental formula, $i^2 = j^2 = k^2 = ijk = -1$, on a stone in Brougham Bridge. Hamilton's "Lectures on Quaternions," published in 1853, and his "Elements of Quaternions," published in 1866, a year after his death, demonstrated the applications of quaternion algebra to geometry and mechanics. The major objection to his algebra was that quaternions were simply too difficult to calculate with. It was the opposition to the use of quaternion algebra by leading mathematicians of the times that led J. W. Gibbs of Yale University, among others, to modify the system of quaternions. Gibbs rejected Hamilton's concept of a single product of two vectors, and he defined an algebra of vectors essentially equivalent to the one studied today.

Hamilton's quaternion algebra depended upon four fundamental units, 1, i, j, and k, whose products are defined by Table 2-1.

Table 2-1

	1	i	j	k
1	1	i	j	k
i	i	-1	k	$-j$
j	j	$-k$	-1	i
k	k	j	$-i$	-1

Note that the product of two of these units is generally not commutative. A **quaternion** is an element of the form $a + bi + cj + dk$, where a, b, c, and d are real numbers; that is, the sum of a scalar a and a *pure quaternion* or *vector* $bi + cj + dk$. Consider the product of two pure quaternions $x_1 i + x_2 j + x_3 k$ and $y_1 i + y_2 j + y_3 k$. Assuming the distributive property of the product with respect to addition, and using Table 2-1, then

$$(x_1 i + x_2 j + x_3 k)(y_1 i + y_2 j + y_3 k) = (x_2 y_3 - x_3 y_2)i$$
$$+ (x_3 y_1 - x_1 y_3)j + (x_1 y_2 - x_2 y_1)k - (x_1 y_1 + x_2 y_2 + x_3 y_3).$$

Therefore the product of two pure quaternions is a quaternion. Note that the two parts of the product correspond to what is considered in vector algebra as the vector product and the scalar product of two vectors; that is, Hamilton's concept of the product of two pure quaternions or vectors is equivalent to the difference of the vector product and the scalar product of the two vectors.

The value of Hamilton's algebra of quaternions rests on two points. First, the study of quaternions led to the development of vector algebra; and second, quaternion algebra destroyed the confines in which algebra had been placed, and illustrated that a consistent algebra was possible whose structure differed from that of the algebra of complex numbers.

Quaternion algebra may also be viewed as a study of *ordered quadruples* of real numbers (a, b, c, d). Then equality, scalar multiplication, addition, and multiplication may be defined:

(i) $(a, b, c, d) = (e, f, g, h)$ if, and only if, $a = e$, $b = f$, $c = g$, and $d = h$;
(ii) $k(a, b, c, d) = (ka, kb, kc, kd)$, for any real scalar k;
(iii) $(a, b, c, d) + (e, f, g, h) = (a + e, b + f, c + g, d + h)$;
(iv) $(a, b, c, d)(e, f, g, h) = (ae - bf - cg - dh,\ af + be + ch - dg,\ ag + ce + df - bh,\ ah + de + bg - cf)$.

Essentially, we may consider a correspondence between quaternions as ordered quadruples of real numbers and quaternions as real multiples of $1, i, j, k$:

$$a + bi + cj + dk \leftrightarrow (a, b, c, d) = a(1, 0, 0, 0) + b(0, 1, 0, 0) + c(0, 0, 1, 0) + d(0, 0, 0, 1),$$

where

$$1 \leftrightarrow (1, 0, 0, 0);\ i \leftrightarrow (0, 1, 0, 0);\ j \leftrightarrow (0, 0, 1, 0);$$

and

$$k \leftrightarrow (0, 0, 0, 1).$$

It should be evident that we may consider three-dimensional vectors as ordered triples of real numbers; that is,

$$x\vec{i} + y\vec{j} + z\vec{k} \leftrightarrow (x, y, z).$$

In general, we may define an **n-dimensional vector** as an ordered n-tuple of real numbers $(a_1, a_2, \ldots, a_n)$. Then the subject of n-dimensional vectors may be developed by considering the following definitions for equality, scalar multiplication, addition, and multiplication, and the properties of real numbers:

(i) $(a_1, a_2, \ldots, a_n) = (b_1, b_2, \ldots, b_n)$ if, and only if, $a_i = b_i$ for $i = 1, 2, \ldots, n$;
(ii) $k(a_1, a_2, \ldots, a_n) = (ka_1, ka_2, \ldots, ka_n)$, for any real scalar k;
(iii) $(a_1, a_2, \ldots, a_n) + (b_1, b_2, \ldots, b_n) = (a_1 + b_1, a_2 + b_2, \ldots, a_n + b_n)$;
(iv) $(a_1, a_2, \ldots, a_n)(b_1, b_2, \ldots, b_n) = a_1b_1 + a_2b_2 + \ldots + a_nb_n$.

A study of vectors as ordered n-tuples of real numbers leads to a generalization of the concept of a vector space for n-dimensions.

Exercises

1. Consider quaternions as ordered quadruples of real numbers and find:
(a) $(2, 3, -1, 4) + (0, 2, 1, -2)$; **(b)** $(3, 1, 2, 0)(2, 1, -1, 4)$;
(c) $3(2, 1, 0, -3)$.

2. If the **conjugate** of a quaternion $x = a + bi + cj + dk$ is defined as $x^* = a - bi - cj - dk$, then find the product of a quaternion and its conjugate; that is, xx^*.

3. Find the multiplicative inverse of the nonzero quaternion $a + bi + cj + dk$, if unity is the identity element. (Hint: See Exercise 2.)

4. Show that the real numbers are embedded within the quaternions by considering both the sum and the product of two quaternions of the form $x + 0i + 0j + 0k$.

5. Show that the complex numbers are embedded within the quaternions by considering both the sum and the product of two quaternions of the form $x + yi + 0j + 0k$.

6. Verify that the product of quaternions is associative for $2 + i + j + k$, $1 - i - j + k$, and $1 + 2i + j - 2k$.

7. Prove that the conjugate of the product of two quaternions is equal to the product of the conjugates of the two quaternions taken in the reverse order; that is, $(xy)^* = y^* x^*$. (See Exercise 2.)

chapter 3

Planes and Lines in Space

3-1 Direction Cosines and Numbers

In this chapter we shall study many of the properties of planes and lines in space through the use of position vectors.

Given a nonzero position vector $\vec{r} = x\vec{i} + y\vec{j} + z\vec{k}$, then, since $\vec{i} \cdot \vec{i} = 1$, $\vec{j} \cdot \vec{i} = 0$, and $\vec{k} \cdot \vec{i} = 0$,

$$\vec{r} \cdot \vec{i} = (x\vec{i} + y\vec{j} + z\vec{k}) \cdot \vec{i} = x.$$

However, by definition, we may express

$$\vec{r} \cdot \vec{i} = |\vec{r}||\vec{i}| \cos(\vec{r}, \vec{i});$$

$$\cos(\vec{r}, \vec{i}) = \frac{\vec{r} \cdot \vec{i}}{|\vec{r}||\vec{i}|} = \frac{x}{|\vec{r}|}. \tag{3-1}$$

In a similar manner it can be shown that

$$\cos(\vec{r}, \vec{j}) = \frac{y}{|\vec{r}|}; \tag{3-2}$$

$$\cos(\vec{r}, \vec{k}) = \frac{z}{|\vec{r}|}. \tag{3-3}$$

Note that in Figure 3-1 angle $(\vec{r}, \vec{i})$ is the angle formed with the position vector $\vec{r}$ on its initial side and the unit vector $\vec{i}$ along the x-axis on its terminal side. Similar statements hold for the angles $(\vec{r}, \vec{j})$ and $(\vec{r}, \vec{k})$, where $\vec{j}$ and $\vec{k}$ are unit vectors along the y- and z-axes, respectively. The

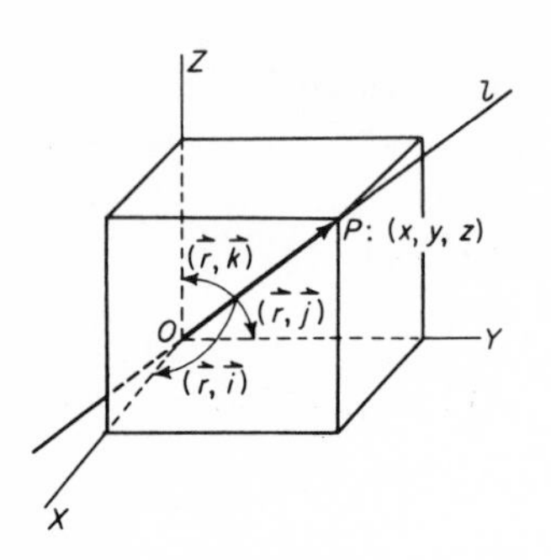

Figure 3-1

angles $(\vec{r}, \vec{i})$, $(\vec{r}, \vec{j})$, and $(\vec{r}, \vec{k})$ are called **direction angles** of $\vec{r}$ and of the line l through the origin and the point P: (x, y, z). The numbers $\cos(\vec{r}, \vec{i})$, $\cos(\vec{r}, \vec{j})$, and $\cos(\vec{r}, \vec{k})$ are called **direction cosines** of the vector $\vec{r}$ and of the line l. Notice that

$$\cos^2(\vec{r}, \vec{i}) + \cos^2(\vec{r}, \vec{j}) + \cos^2(\vec{r}, \vec{k}) = \frac{x^2 + y^2 + z^2}{|\vec{r}|^2} = 1; \tag{3-4}$$

that is, *the sum of the squares of the direction cosines of any nonzero position vector $\vec{r}$ is equal to 1*. Hence, the three direction cosines are not independent. If two of them are given, then the numerical value of the third may be determined from equation (3-4). Furthermore, if three angles are to be considered as direction angles of a vector or of a line, the sum of the squares of their cosines must be equal to 1.

In rectangular cartesian coordinate form the direction cosines of vector $\vec{r}$ are given by the ordered triple

$$\left(\frac{x}{\sqrt{x^2 + y^2 + z^2}} : \frac{y}{\sqrt{x^2 + y^2 + z^2}} : \frac{z}{\sqrt{x^2 + y^2 + z^2}}\right) \tag{3-5}$$

whose members are proportional to the components x, y, and z of vector $\vec{r}$.

Now, let $\vec{r}_1 = x_1\vec{i} + y_1\vec{j} + z_1\vec{k}$ and $\vec{r}_2 = x_2\vec{i} + y_2\vec{j} + z_2\vec{k}$ be any two nonzero position vectors. Let $(l_1 : m_1 : n_1)$ and $(l_2 : m_2 : n_2)$ be their respective direction cosines. Then the cosine of the angle between the two position vectors may be derived as follows:

$$\cos(\vec{r}_1, \vec{r}_2) = \frac{\vec{r}_1 \cdot \vec{r}_2}{|\vec{r}_1||\vec{r}_2|} = \frac{x_1x_2 + y_1y_2 + z_1z_2}{|\vec{r}_1||\vec{r}_2|},$$

$$\cos(\vec{r}_1, \vec{r}_2) = \frac{x_1}{|\vec{r}_1|}\frac{x_2}{|\vec{r}_2|} + \frac{y_1}{|\vec{r}_1|}\frac{y_2}{|\vec{r}_2|} + \frac{z_1}{|\vec{r}_1|}\frac{z_2}{|\vec{r}_2|},$$

$$\cos(\vec{r}_1, \vec{r}_2) = l_1l_2 + m_1m_2 + n_1n_2. \tag{3-6}$$

From the first of the last three equations, we obtain in rectangular cartesian coordinate form

$$\cos(\vec{r}_1, \vec{r}_2) = \frac{x_1x_2 + y_1y_2 + z_1z_2}{\sqrt{x_1^2 + y_1^2 + z_1^2}\sqrt{x_2^2 + y_2^2 + z_2^2}}. \tag{3-7}$$

Two nonzero position vectors are perpendicular if, and only if, the angle $(\vec{r}_1, \vec{r}_2)$ has measure 90°. Since $\cos 90° = 0$, the condition for perpendicularity may be expressed from (3-6) and (3-7) as either

$$l_1l_2 + m_1m_2 + n_1n_2 = 0 \tag{3-8}$$

or

$$x_1x_2 + y_1y_2 + z_1z_2 = 0. \tag{3-9}$$

The components x, y, and z of $\vec{r}$ are sometimes called **direction numbers** of the position vector and may be written as $(x:y:z)$. Any ordered set of three numbers, that can be obtained from these by multiplying all of them by the same positive constant k, is also a set of direction numbers for the vector $\vec{r}$, in that they define the direction of the vector. Any ordered set of three numbers that can be obtained from $(x:y:z)$ by multiplying all of them by the same nonzero constant k is a set of direction numbers for any line parallel to $\vec{r}$. Note that a line is generally not oriented.

Consider a line passing through P_1: (x_1, y_1, z_1) and P_2: (x_2, y_2, z_2), with the length of the line segment P_1P_2 equal to d. Then the position vector $(x_2 - x_1)\vec{i} + (y_2 - y_1)\vec{j} + (z_2 - z_1)\vec{k}$ is equivalent to $\overrightarrow{P_1P_2}$. The direction cosines of the position vector and $\overrightarrow{P_1P_2}$ are then given by the equations

$$\cos\alpha = \frac{x_2 - x_1}{d}, \qquad \cos\beta = \frac{y_2 - y_1}{d}, \qquad \cos\gamma = \frac{z_2 - z_1}{d}, \tag{3-10}$$

where α, β, and γ are the angles the position vector makes with the positive x-, y-, and z-axes, respectively. The direction cosines of the line P_1P_2 may be taken as those of any position vector parallel to it. Note that since a position vector equivalent to $\overrightarrow{P_2P_1}$ could have been determined, then there exist two sets of direction cosines for each line but only one set of direction cosines for any position vector parallel to the line.

Example Find a set of direction cosines for the line through A: $(3, -2, 4)$ and B: $(5, -3, 2)$.

The position vector equivalent to $\overrightarrow{AB}$ is $(5 - 3)\vec{i} + (-3 + 2)\vec{j} + (2 - 4)\vec{k}$; that is, $2\vec{i} - \vec{j} - 2\vec{k}$. Its direction cosines are equal to each of its components divided by the square root of the sum of the squares of its components. Since its components are 2, -1, and -2; $\sqrt{2^2 + (-1)^2 + (-2)^2} = 3$; $\cos\alpha = \frac{2}{3}$; $\cos\beta = -\frac{1}{3}$; $\cos\gamma = -\frac{2}{3}$. The direction cosines of the line AB may be taken as $(\frac{2}{3}: -\frac{1}{3}: -\frac{2}{3})$. Since line AB is also parallel to $\overrightarrow{BA}$ with direction cosines $(-\frac{2}{3}: \frac{1}{3}: \frac{2}{3})$, this ordered triple represents another set of direction cosines of the line. One set of direction numbers for the line is $(2: -1: -2)$.

In general, any ordered set of scalars $(2k: -k: -2k)$, where $k \neq 0$, represents a set of direction numbers for line AB.

Exercises

In Exercises 1 through 4 use points A: (1, −5, 3) and B: (4, 7, −1).

1. Find the direction cosines of $\overrightarrow{AB}$.

2. Find the two sets of direction cosines for line AB.

3. Find the general form of the direction numbers of $\overrightarrow{AB}$.

4. Find the general form of the direction numbers of line AB.

5. Given the following sets of angles, choose those which may be a set of direction angles:
(**a**) $(30°: 45°: 60°)$; (**b**) $(120°: 135°: 60°)$;
(**c**) $(30°: 150°: 0°)$; (**d**) $(0°: 0°: 90°)$.

6. Determine which of the following sets of values may be a set of direction cosines:
(**a**) $(\frac{2}{3}: \frac{1}{3}: -\frac{2}{3})$; (**b**) $(1: -\frac{1}{2}: \frac{1}{2})$;
(**c**) $(\frac{5}{8}: \frac{1}{3}: \frac{1}{2})$; (**d**) $(0: 1: 0)$;
(**e**) $(\cos\theta: \sin\theta: 0)$.

7. If two direction angles of a vector are 60° and 60°, find (**a**) a third direction angle of the vector; (**b**) a third direction angle of any line parallel to the vector.

8. Find the direction cosines of the unit vectors on the coordinate axes: (**a**) $\vec{i}$; (**b**) $\vec{j}$; (**c**) $\vec{k}$.

9. If a line has a set of direction numbers $(1: 0: -3)$, find a set of direction cosines of the line.

10. Show that the direction cosines of a line in the xy-plane are a special case of the direction cosines of a line in space.

11. Given the point $(2, 1, -4)$ on a line with a set of direction numbers $(3: -1: 1)$, find three other points on the line.

12. If the direction cosines of two intersecting lines are $(1/2: \sqrt{2}/2: 1/2)$ and $(-1/2: 1/2: \sqrt{2}/2)$, find the angles between the two lines.

13. If a set of direction numbers of two intersecting lines are $(1: 1: 4)$ and $(0: 1: -1)$, find the acute angle between the two lines.

14. Show that the lines AB and CD are parallel where $A: (2, 3, 6)$, $B: (4, 1, 2)$, $C: (3, 0, 1)$, and $D: (2, 1, 3)$.

15. Determine the cosine of the angle between the diagonal of a cube and one of its intersecting edges.

3-2 Equation of a Plane

There are several ways of determining a plane in space. For example, a plane may be described or specified by three given points on the plane which do not lie on a single straight line, or by a line and a point on the plane, providing the point does not lie on the line, or by other means. A convenient way of describing a plane is by designating a point through which it passes and a vector which is perpendicular (normal) to the plane. To determine the vector equation of such a plane, let $\vec{n}$ be a vector normal to the plane (Figure 3-2).

Let $P: (x, y, z)$ be a general point on the plane. Since $\overrightarrow{P_0P}$ is perpendicular to $\vec{n}$,

$$\overrightarrow{P_0P} \cdot \vec{n} = 0, \qquad (3\text{-}11)$$

$$(\overrightarrow{OP} - \overrightarrow{OP_0}) \cdot \vec{n} = 0. \qquad (3\text{-}12)$$

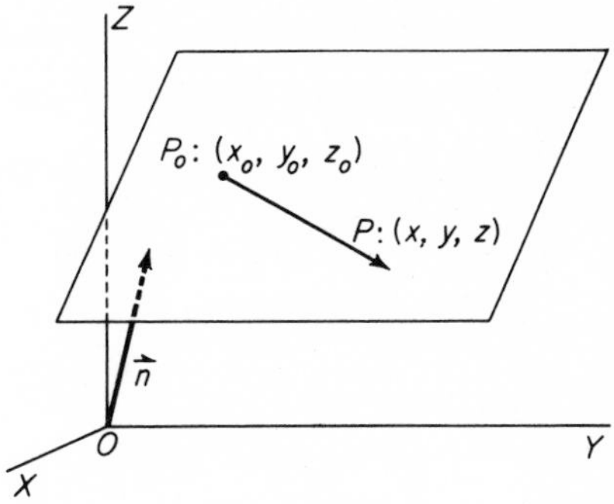

Figure 3-2

Equations (3-11) and (3-12) represent vector forms of the equation of the plane through P_0: (x_0, y_0, z_0) with vector $\vec{n}$ normal to the plane.

The general rectangular cartesian coordinate form of the equation of a plane can be obtained from the vector form (3-12). Let $\vec{n} = a\vec{i} + b\vec{j} + c\vec{k}$. Then, since

$$\overrightarrow{OP} = x\vec{i} + y\vec{j} + z\vec{k} \qquad \text{and} \qquad \overrightarrow{OP_0} = x_0\vec{i} + y_0\vec{j} + z_0\vec{k},$$

$$\overrightarrow{OP} - \overrightarrow{OP_0} = (x - x_0)\vec{i} + (y - y_0)\vec{j} + (z - z_0)\vec{k},$$

$$a(x - x_0) + b(y - y_0) + c(z - z_0) = 0, \qquad (3\text{-}13)$$

and

$$ax + by + cz + d = 0, \qquad (3\text{-}14)$$

where $d = -ax_0 - by_0 - cz_0$. This is the general rectangular cartesian coordinate form of the equation of a plane with arbitrary constants a, b, c, and d. Hereafter the expression **coordinate form** shall be used to mean rectangular cartesian coordinate form.

Equation (3-13) is sometimes called the **point-direction number form of the equation of a plane,** since it involves the coordinates of a point on the plane and the direction numbers of a vector normal to the plane.

It is important to remember that the coefficients a, b, and c of x, y, and z, respectively, in any equation of a plane, are the components of a vector normal to the plane.

If $abcd \neq 0$, the general equation may be written in the form

$$\frac{x}{e} + \frac{y}{f} + \frac{z}{g} = 1, \qquad (3\text{-}15)$$

where $e = -d/a$, $f = -d/b$, and $g = -d/c$. This equation is called the **intercept form of the equation of a plane** since e, f, and g are the x, y, and z intercepts, respectively, of the given plane. That is to say, the given plane intersects the coordinate axes at points whose coordinates are $(e, 0, 0)$, $(0, f, 0)$, and $(0, 0, g)$.

Example 1 Find the equation of the plane through N: $(-2, 1, 2)$ and perpendicular to $\overrightarrow{ON}$.

Let P: (x, y, z) be a general point on the plane through N perpendicular to $\overrightarrow{ON}$. Then $\overrightarrow{ON}$ and $\overrightarrow{NP}$ are perpendicular to each other and $\overrightarrow{ON} \cdot \overrightarrow{NP} = 0$. Since

$$\overrightarrow{ON} = -2\vec{i} + \vec{j} + 2\vec{k}$$

and

$$\begin{aligned} \overrightarrow{NP} = \overrightarrow{OP} - \overrightarrow{ON} &= (x\vec{i} + y\vec{j} + z\vec{k}) - (-2\vec{i} + \vec{j} + 2\vec{k}) \\ &= (x + 2)\vec{i} + (y - 1)\vec{j} + (z - 2)\vec{k}, \\ \overrightarrow{ON} \cdot \overrightarrow{NP} &= -2(x + 2) + (y - 1) + 2(z - 2) = 0; \end{aligned}$$

that is,

$$2x - y - 2z + 9 = 0.$$

Example 2 Find the equation of a plane which passes through the point P: $(4, 2, 1)$ and is parallel to the plane $2x + 3y - z + 5 = 0$.

A vector normal to one of two parallel planes is a vector normal to the other plane. Therefore, the components 2, 3, and -1 of a vector normal to the given plane are also the components of a vector normal to the desired plane, and thus are the coefficients of x, y, and z, respectively, of the plane to be determined. It remains to find d in the equation

$$2x + 3y - z + d = 0.$$

Since P lies on the plane, the coordinates of P satisfy the equation of the plane; that is,

$$2(4) + 3(2) - (1) + d = 0, \qquad \text{and} \qquad d = -13.$$

Therefore, the equation of the desired plane is

$$2x + 3y - z - 13 = 0.$$

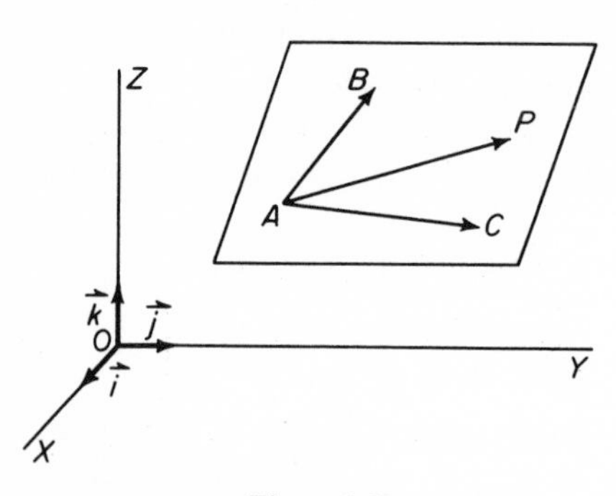

Figure 3-3

A plane may also be determined if three distinct noncollinear points of the plane are known. Several vector forms of the equation of the plane may be found. One vector form depends upon the concept of a set of linearly dependent vectors (§1-5).

Let A: (x_1, y_1, z_1), B: (x_2, y_2, z_2) and C: (x_3, y_3, z_3) be three distinct noncollinear points. Consider P: (x, y, z) a general point on the plane ABC (Figure 3-3). Since $\overrightarrow{AP}$ lies on the plane determined by $\overrightarrow{AB}$ and $\overrightarrow{AC}$,

$$\overrightarrow{AP} = m\overrightarrow{AB} + n\overrightarrow{AC} \tag{3-16}$$

represents a vector form of the equation of the plane. Equation (3-16) may also be written as

$$\overrightarrow{OP} - \overrightarrow{OA} = m(\overrightarrow{OB} - \overrightarrow{OA}) + n(\overrightarrow{OC} - \overrightarrow{OA}) \tag{3-17}$$

or

$$\overrightarrow{OP} = (1 - m - n)\overrightarrow{OA} + m\overrightarrow{OB} + n\overrightarrow{OC}. \tag{3-18}$$

Now,

$$\overrightarrow{OP} = x\vec{i} + y\vec{j} + z\vec{k}, \qquad \overrightarrow{OA} = x_1\vec{i} + y_1\vec{j} + z_1\vec{k},$$
$$\overrightarrow{OB} = x_2\vec{i} + y_2\vec{j} + z_2\vec{k}, \qquad \text{and} \qquad \overrightarrow{OC} = x_3\vec{i} + y_3\vec{j} + z_3\vec{k}.$$

The corresponding components, after substituting in equation (3-18), must be equal:

$$\begin{cases} x = (1 - m - n)x_1 + mx_2 + nx_3, \\ y = (1 - m - n)y_1 + my_2 + ny_3, \\ z = (1 - m - n)z_1 + mz_2 + nz_3. \end{cases} \tag{3-19}$$

The equations of (3-19) are one set of **parametric equations of a plane** through A, B, and C with parameters m and n. Each point of the plane corresponds to an ordered pair of values (m, n) of the parameters.

A second vector form of the equation of a plane through three distinct noncollinear points depends upon the concept of the scalar triple product. In Figure 3-3, $\overrightarrow{AB} \times \overrightarrow{AC}$ is a vector perpendicular to the plane determined by A, B, and C; $\overrightarrow{AP}$ lies on the plane. Hence

$$\overrightarrow{AP} \cdot (\overrightarrow{AB} \times \overrightarrow{AC}) = 0. \tag{3-20}$$

Equation (3-20) is another vector form of the equation of the plane ABC. In terms of the rectangular cartesian coordinates of the points A, B, and C, equation (3-20) may be expressed in the form

$$\begin{vmatrix} x - x_1 & y - y_1 & z - z_1 \\ x_2 - x_1 & y_2 - y_1 & z_2 - z_1 \\ x_3 - x_1 & y_3 - y_1 & z_3 - z_1 \end{vmatrix} = 0. \tag{3-21}$$

Example 3 Find a set of parametric equations of the plane through A: $(3, -1, 2)$, B: $(1, 4, 0)$, and C: $(0, -2, 1)$.

By equations (3-19)

$$\begin{cases} x = (1 - m - n)\ (3) + m(1) + \ n(0), \\ y = (1 - m - n)(-1) + m(4) + n(-2), \\ z = (1 - m - n)\ (2) + m(0) + \ n(1); \end{cases}$$

that is,

$$\begin{cases} x = 3 - 2m - 3n, \\ y = -1 + 5m - n, \\ z = 2 - 2m - n. \end{cases}$$

Note that equations (3-19) were derived from equation (3-18). Therefore, letting $m = n = 0$, the coordinates of A should be obtained; letting $m = 1$ and $n = 0$, the coordinates of B should be obtained; letting $m = 0$ and $n = 1$, the coordinates of C should be obtained. This procedure serves as a check for the validity of the set of parametric equations derived.

Furthermore, note that a set of parametric equations of a plane is not unique. For example, a simple exchange of the roles of the points A and B or A and C in equation (3-16) yields a different set of parametric equations.

Example 4 Find the coordinate form of the equation of the plane through the points A: (1, 2, 0), B: (3, −1, 2), and C: (2, 4, 3).

Let P be any point of the plane determined by A, B, and C. Then $\overrightarrow{AB} = 2\vec{i} - 3\vec{j} + 2\vec{k}$, $\overrightarrow{AC} = \vec{i} + 2\vec{j} + 3\vec{k}$, $\overrightarrow{AP} = (x-1)\vec{i} + (y-2)\vec{j} + z\vec{k}$, and

$$\overrightarrow{AP}\cdot(\overrightarrow{AB} \times \overrightarrow{AC}) = \begin{vmatrix} x-1 & y-2 & z \\ 2 & -3 & 2 \\ 1 & 2 & 3 \end{vmatrix} = 0.$$

Then

$$-13(x-1) - 4(y-2) + 7z = 0;$$

that is,

$$13x + 4y - 7z - 21 = 0.$$

Exercises

1. Find the equation of the plane through N: (3, −2, 1) and perpendicular to $\overrightarrow{ON}$.
2. Find the equation of the plane through N: (2, 1, −1) and perpendicular to $\vec{r} = \vec{i} + \vec{j} - 3\vec{k}$.
3. Find the equation of the plane through N: (7, −4, 3) and perpendicular to line AB where A: (2, 0, −1) and B: (5, 6, 0).
4. Determine the equation of the plane which passes through P: (1, 2, −2) and is parallel to the plane $x + 4y - 2z = 0$.
5. Determine a set of parametric equations of the plane through A: (1, 2, 0), B: (−3, 2, 4), and C: (5, 1, −1).
6. Find the general coordinate form of the equation of the plane in Exercise 5.
7. State the condition that must exist in each case between the coefficients of the equation of the plane $ax + by + cz + d = 0$ in order that:
   (a) the plane may have intercept 2 on the y-axis;
   (b) the plane may have equal intercepts on the y- and z-axes;

(c) the plane may have equal intercepts on all three coordinates axes;
(d) the plane may be parallel to the plane $2x - y + z - 7 = 0$;
(e) the plane may be perpendicular to the vector $\vec{i} + 3\vec{j} + 5\vec{k}$;
(f) the plane may pass through the origin;
(g) the plane may pass through the point $(2, -1, 4)$;
(h) the plane may be parallel to the y-axis;
(i) the plane may be parallel to the yz-plane;
(j) the plane may contain the z-axis.

8. Show that the points A: $(1, -1, 1)$, B: $(2, 0, 0)$, C: $(-1, 1, 5)$, and D: $(0, 0, 3)$ are coplanar.

9. Determine the equation of the plane through A: $(2, 1, 5)$, B: $(3, -2, 4)$, and C: $(1, -3, 3)$.

10. Find a vector form of the equation of the plane through the origin parallel to the position vectors $\overrightarrow{OA}$ and $\overrightarrow{OB}$.

11. Find a vector form of the equation of the plane through the point C and parallel to the position vectors $\overrightarrow{OA}$ and $\overrightarrow{OB}$.

3-3 Equation of a Sphere

A sphere is the locus of points in space which are equidistant from one fixed point, the center. Let S be a sphere of radius a with center at a point C: (x_0, y_0, z_0), as shown in Figure 3-4. If P: (x, y, z) is a general point on the sphere S, and $\overrightarrow{OP}$ is the position vector of this point while $\overrightarrow{OC}$ is the position vector of the center C, then

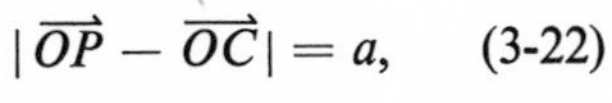

$$|\overrightarrow{OP} - \overrightarrow{OC}| = a, \qquad (3\text{-}22)$$

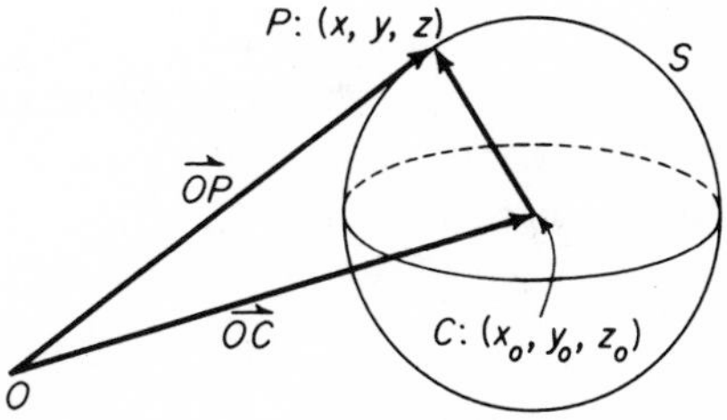

Figure 3-4

and

$$(\overrightarrow{OP} - \overrightarrow{OC})\cdot(\overrightarrow{OP} - \overrightarrow{OC}) = a^2. \quad (3\text{-}23)$$

Equation (3-23) represents a vector form of the equation of sphere S.

Since $\overrightarrow{OP} = x\vec{i} + y\vec{j} + z\vec{k}$ and $\overrightarrow{OC} = x_0\vec{i} + y_0\vec{j} + z_0\vec{k}$, then $\overrightarrow{OP} - \overrightarrow{OC} = (x - x_0)\vec{i} + (y - y_0)\vec{j} + (z - z_0)\vec{k}$. Therefore, by Theorem 2-7, equation (3-23) may be expressed in terms of rectangular cartesian coordinates as

$$(x - x_0)^2 + (y - y_0)^2 + (z - z_0)^2 = a^2. \qquad (3\text{-}24)$$

Equation (3-24) is the coordinate form of the equation of a sphere with center at C: (x_0, y_0, z_0) and radius equal to a.

Example 1 Find the equation of the sphere with center at C: $(3, -1, 2)$ and radius equal to 5.

Let P: (x, y, z) be a general point on the sphere. Then the equation of the sphere in vector form is given by equation (3-23),

$$(\overrightarrow{OP} - \overrightarrow{OC})\cdot(\overrightarrow{OP} - \overrightarrow{OC}) = a^2,$$

where

$$\overrightarrow{OP} = x\vec{i} + y\vec{j} + z\vec{k},\ \overrightarrow{OC} = 3\vec{i} - \vec{j} + 2\vec{k},\quad \text{and}\quad a = 5.$$

Therefore,

$$(x - 3)^2 + (y + 1)^2 + (z - 2)^2 = 25,$$

that is,

$$x^2 + y^2 + z^2 - 6x + 2y - 4z - 11 = 0,$$

is the coordinate form of the equation of the sphere.

Example 2 Find the equation of the sphere with center at the origin and radius equal to a.

If P: (x, y, z) is a general point on the sphere, then a vector form of the equation of the sphere with center at the origin and radius equal to a is

$$\overrightarrow{OP}\cdot\overrightarrow{OP} = a^2.$$

In coordinate form this equation may be expressed as

$$x^2 + y^2 + z^2 = a^2.$$

The equation of the plane π which intersects a given sphere S at one, and only one, point P is said to be tangent to the sphere at the given point. To determine the equation of such a plane, let P: (x, y, z) be a general point on the plane π, let P_1: (x_1, y_1, z_1) be the point of tangency, and let C: (x_0, y_0, z_0) be the center of the sphere S as shown in Figure 3-5. Then

$$(\overrightarrow{OP} - \overrightarrow{OP_1})\cdot(\overrightarrow{OC} - \overrightarrow{OP_1}) = 0, \tag{3-25}$$

since the radius from C to P_1 will be perpendicular to every line in π through P_1. Equation (3-25) is a vector form of the equation of the tangent plane π. Since $\overrightarrow{OP} = x\vec{i} + y\vec{j} + z\vec{k}$, $\overrightarrow{OP_1} = x_1\vec{i} + y_1\vec{j} + z_1\vec{k}$, and $\overrightarrow{OC} = x_0\vec{i} + y_0\vec{j} + z_0\vec{k}$, then $\overrightarrow{OP} - \overrightarrow{OP_1} = (x - x_1)\vec{i} + (y - y_1)\vec{j} + (z - z_1)\vec{k}$, and $\overrightarrow{OC} - \overrightarrow{OP_1} = (x_0 - x_1)\vec{i} + (y_0 - y_1)\vec{j} + (z_0 - z_1)\vec{k}$. Therefore the equation

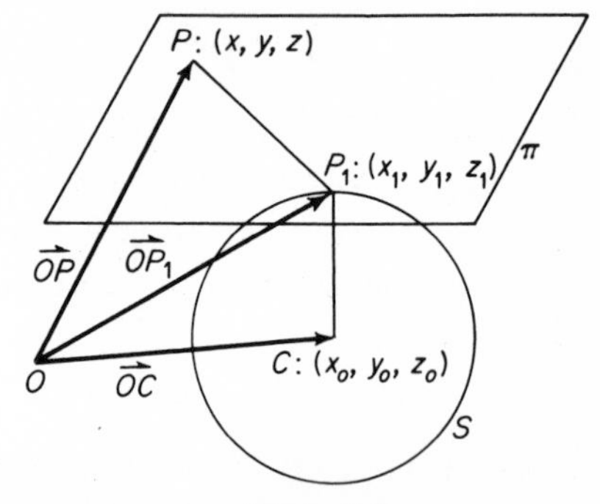

Figure 3-5

$$(x - x_1)(x_0 - x_1) + (y - y_1)(y_0 - y_1) + (z - z_1)(z_0 - z_1) = 0 \quad (3\text{-}26)$$

represents the coordinate form of the equation of the plane π tangent at (x_1, y_1, z_1) to the sphere with center at the point (x_0, y_0, z_0).

Example 3 Find the equation of the plane tangent at P_1: (2, 4, 1) to the sphere with center at C: (3, −1, 2).

The tangent plane is expressed by equation (3-25) as

$$(\overrightarrow{OP} - \overrightarrow{OP_1})\cdot(\overrightarrow{OC} - \overrightarrow{OP_1}) = 0,$$

where

$$\overrightarrow{OP} = x\vec{i} + y\vec{j} + z\vec{k},\ \overrightarrow{OC} = 3\vec{i} - \vec{j} + 2\vec{k},$$

and

$$\overrightarrow{OP_1} = 2\vec{i} + 4\vec{j} + \vec{k}.$$

Since

$$\overrightarrow{OP} - \overrightarrow{OP_1} = (x - 2)\vec{i} + (y - 4)\vec{j} + (z - 1)\vec{k},$$

and

$$\overrightarrow{OC} - \overrightarrow{OP_1} = \vec{i} - 5\vec{j} + \vec{k},$$

then

$$(\overrightarrow{OP} - \overrightarrow{OP_1})\cdot(\overrightarrow{OC} - \overrightarrow{OP_1}) = (x - 2) - 5(y - 4) + (z - 1).$$

Therefore,

$$x - 5y + z + 17 = 0$$

is the equation of the plane tangent at P_1: (2, 4, 1) to the sphere with center at C: (3, −1, 2).

Example 4 Find the equation of the tangent plane to the sphere with center at the origin and radius equal to a.

Let $P_1: (x_1, y_1, z_1)$ be any point on the sphere with center at the origin and radius equal to a. Using equation (3-26), where $C: (x_0, y_0, z_0)$ is the origin,

$$(x - x_1)(-x_1) + (y - y_1)(-y_1) + (z - z_1)(-z_1) = 0,$$

$$x_1x + y_1y + z_1z = x_1^2 + y_1^2 + z_1^2,$$

and

$$x_1x + y_1y + z_1z = a^2. \quad (3\text{-}27)$$

Equation (3-27) represents the coordinate form of the equation of the tangent plane to the sphere with center at the origin, radius equal to a, and tangent point at $P_1: (x_1, y_1, z_1)$.

Exercises

1. Find the equation of the sphere with center at C: (1, −2, 4) and radius equal to 3.

2. Find the equation of the sphere with center at C: $(0, 0, a)$ and radius equal to a.

3. Find the equation of the plane tangent at P_1: $(2, 6, 5)$ to the sphere with center at C: $(1, 5, 3)$.

4. Find the center and radius of the sphere whose equation is $x^2 + y^2 + z^2 - 6x + 6y - 2z + 3 = 0$.

5. Determine the equation of the plane tangent at P_1: $(2, 3, 0)$ to the sphere $x^2 + y^2 + z^2 + 4x - 6y = 3$.

6. Determine the equation of the sphere with diameter AB where A: $(-4, 5, 0)$ and B: $(4, 1, 8)$.

7. If the line segment joining A: $(-2, -1, 2)$ and B: $(2, 1, 2)$ subtends a right angle at P: (x, y, z) when P does not coincide with A or B, find a relation among the coordinates of P.

8. If the coordinates of the mid-point of line segment OP satisfy the equation $x^2 + y^2 + z^2 = 8$, determine the value of k such that the coordinates of P satisfy the equation $x^2 + y^2 + z^2 = k$.

9. Determine the equation of the plane tangent at $(1, 0, 0)$ to the sphere $x^2 + y^2 + z^2 = 1$.

3-4 Angle Between Two Planes

When two planes intersect, two pairs of supplementary dihedral angles are formed. The measures of these dihedral angles are the same as the measures of the corresponding angles formed by the intersection of vectors normal to the planes (Figure 3-6).

To determine a formula for the angle between two intersecting planes let the equations of the planes be $a_1x + b_1y + c_1z = d_1$ and $a_2x + b_2y + c_2z = d_2$. The vectors $\vec{n_1} = a_1\vec{i} + b_1\vec{j} + c_1\vec{k}$ and $\vec{n_2} = a_2\vec{i} + b_2\vec{j} + c_2\vec{k}$ are perpendicular to these two planes, respectively. The angle between these vectors may be found by using the relationship

$$\vec{n_1} \cdot \vec{n_2} = |\vec{n_1}|\,|\vec{n_2}| \cos(\vec{n_1}, \vec{n_2}).$$

It follows that

$$\cos(\vec{n_1}, \vec{n_2}) = \pm \frac{\vec{n_1} \cdot \vec{n_2}}{|\vec{n_1}|\,|\vec{n_2}|}, \qquad (3\text{-}28)$$

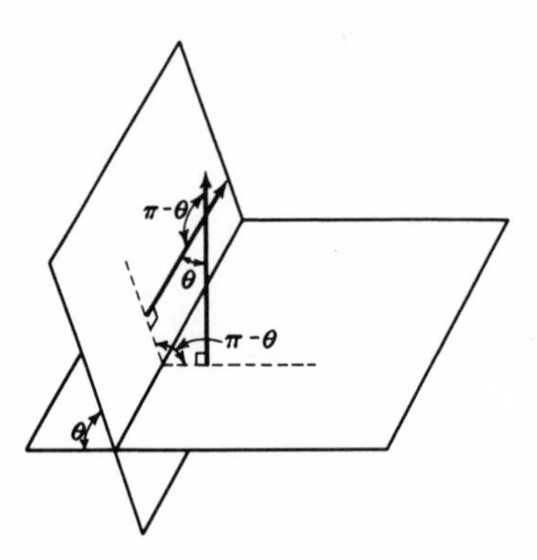

Figure 3-6

where the two algebraic signs are considered in order to obtain the two supplementary angles. In terms of the components

$$\cos(\overrightarrow{n_1}, \overrightarrow{n_2}) = \pm \frac{a_1a_2 + b_1b_2 + c_1c_2}{\sqrt{a_1^2 + b_1^2 + c_1^2}\sqrt{a_2^2 + b_2^2 + c_2^2}}. \tag{3-29}$$

Note that the planes are perpendicular if $\cos(\overrightarrow{n_1}, \overrightarrow{n_2}) = 0$; that is, if

$$\overrightarrow{n_1} \cdot \overrightarrow{n_2} = 0. \tag{3-30}$$

In coordinate form, the planes are perpendicular if

$$a_1a_2 + b_1b_2 + c_1c_2 = 0. \tag{3-31}$$

The planes are parallel if the vectors normal to the planes are parallel. This condition may be expressed by the relationship

$$\frac{a_1}{a_2} = \frac{b_1}{b_2} = \frac{c_1}{c_2} = t, \tag{3-32}$$

for some scalar t.

Example 1 Find the measures of the dihedral angles formed by the planes $-x + 2y + 2z = 10$ and $x + y + 4z = 7$.

The vectors normal to the planes are $\overrightarrow{n_1} = -\vec{i} + 2\vec{j} + 2\vec{k}$ and $\overrightarrow{n_2} = \vec{i} + \vec{j} + 4\vec{k}$.

Then,

$$\begin{aligned}\cos(\overrightarrow{n_1}, \overrightarrow{n_2}) &= \pm \frac{\overrightarrow{n_1} \cdot \overrightarrow{n_2}}{|\overrightarrow{n_1}||\overrightarrow{n_2}|} \\ &= \pm \frac{(-1)(1) + (2)(1) + (2)(4)}{\sqrt{(-1)^2 + (2)^2 + (2)^2}\sqrt{(1)^2 + (1)^2 + (4)^2}} \\ &= \pm \frac{9}{\sqrt{9}\sqrt{18}} = \pm \frac{1}{\sqrt{2}}.\end{aligned}$$

Hence the measures of the dihedral angles formed by the planes are 45° and 135°.

Example 2 Show that the planes $2x - y + 2z = 3$ and $2x + 2y - z = 7$ are perpendicular.

The vectors $\overrightarrow{n_1} = 2\vec{i} - \vec{j} + 2\vec{k}$ and $\overrightarrow{n_2} = 2\vec{i} + 2\vec{j} - \vec{k}$ are normal to the planes. Since $\overrightarrow{n_1} \cdot \overrightarrow{n_2} = (2)(2) + (-1)(2) + (2)(-1) = 0$, the planes are perpendicular.

Exercises

1. Find the measures of the dihedral angles formed by the planes $2x - 4y - 4z - 5 = 0$ and $x + 4y + z - 3 = 0$.
2. Show that the planes $x + 3y + z + 4 = 0$ and $2x - y + z + 2 = 0$ are perpendicular.
3. Show that the planes $3x - 2y + z + 7 = 0$ and $9x - 6y + 3z + 10 = 0$ are parallel.

4. Find the value of c for which the planes $3x - 4y + cz = 0$ and $2x - 3y + 6z - 1 = 0$ are perpendicular.

5. Find the measure of the acute angle between the planes $x + 2y + 2z - 1 = 0$ and $3x - 4y - 5z = 0$.

6. Determine the equation of the plane containing the points A: $(1, -1, -2)$ and B: $(4, 2, 2)$, and which is perpendicular to the plane $3x + y - 2z = 12$.

3-5 Distance Between a Point and a Plane

A formula for the shortest distance between a point and a line on a plane was determined in §2-3. In a similar manner, the shortest distance between a point and a plane in space may be determined. Let P_1: (x_1, y_1, z_1) be any point in space, and let P_0: (x_0, y_0, z_0) be any point on the plane $ax + by + cz + d = 0$. The shortest distance r between the point and the plane is equal to the magnitude of the projection of $\overrightarrow{P_0P_1}$ on $\vec{n}$, a unit vector normal to the plane as shown in Figure 3-7. Therefore

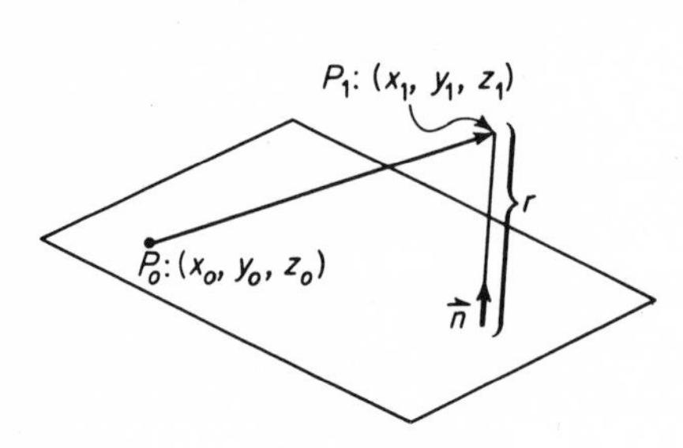

Figure 3-7

$$\begin{aligned}
\vec{r} &= |\overrightarrow{P_0P_1} \cdot \vec{n}| \\
&= \left| [(x_1 - x_0)\vec{i} + (y_1 - y_0)\vec{j} + (z_1 - z_0)\vec{k}] \cdot \frac{a\vec{i} + b\vec{j} + c\vec{k}}{\sqrt{a^2 + b^2 + c^2}} \right| \\
&= \frac{|a(x_1 - x_0) + b(y_1 - y_0) + c(z_1 - z_0)|}{\sqrt{a^2 + b^2 + c^2}} \\
&= \frac{|ax_1 + by_1 + cz_1 - ax_0 - by_0 - cz_0|}{\sqrt{a^2 + b^2 + c^2}}.
\end{aligned}$$

But, $d = -ax_0 - by_0 - cz_0$, since P_0: (x_0, y_0, z_0) lies on the plane. Therefore,

$$r = \frac{|ax_1 + by_1 + cz_1 + d|}{\sqrt{a^2 + b^2 + c^2}}. \tag{3-33}$$

Example 1 Find the shortest distance between the point P_1: $(1, -2, -4)$ and the plane $2x + 2y - z = 11$.

By equation (3-33), the distance r is given as

$$\begin{aligned}
r &= \frac{|(2)(1) + (2)(-2) + (-1)(-4) + (-11)|}{\sqrt{2^2 + 2^2 + (-1)^2}} \\
&= \frac{|-9|}{3} = 3.
\end{aligned}$$

An alternate approach is to consider the problem in vector form; that is, essentially, to derive equation (3-33) for this particular case. Choose any point on the plane, say P_0: (3, 2, −1). Then $\overrightarrow{P_0P_1} = -2\vec{i} - 4\vec{j} - 3\vec{k}$. A unit vector normal to the plane is $\vec{n} = \frac{2}{3}\vec{i} + \frac{2}{3}\vec{j} - \frac{1}{3}\vec{k}$. Since r is equal to the magnitude of the projection of $\overrightarrow{P_0P_1}$ on $\vec{n}$, then

$$r = |\overrightarrow{P_0P_1} \cdot \vec{n}| = |(-2)(\tfrac{2}{3}) + (-4)(\tfrac{2}{3}) + (-3)(-\tfrac{1}{3})| = 3;$$

that is, 3 units.

Example 2 Find a formula for the shortest distance between the origin and any plane $ax + by + cz + d = 0$.

By equation (3-33) where P_1: (x_1, y_1, z_1) is the origin,

$$r = \frac{|d|}{\sqrt{a^2 + b^2 + c^2}}. \tag{3-34}$$

If two planes

$$a_1x + b_1y + c_1z + d_1 = 0,$$
$$a_2x + b_2y + c_2z + d_2 = 0$$

are parallel or coincide, then by §3-4

$$\frac{a_1}{a_2} = \frac{b_1}{b_2} = \frac{c_1}{c_2} = t.$$

Therefore, by multiplying the equation of the second plane by t, the variables x, y, and z in the equations of the two planes will contain identical coefficients. That is, the equations become

$$\begin{aligned} a_1x + b_1y + c_1z + d_1 &= 0, \\ a_1x + b_1y + c_1z + d_3 &= 0, \end{aligned} \tag{3-35}$$

where $d_3 = td_2$, but is not necessarily equal to d_1 unless the planes coincide. To find the distance r between these planes, take any point P_1: (x_1, y_1, z_1) on the plane $a_1x + b_1y + c_1z + d_1 = 0$. The distance r between the point P_1 and the plane $a_1x + b_1y + c_1z + d_3 = 0$ is given by the expression

$$r = \frac{|a_1x_1 + b_1y_1 + c_1z_1 + d_3|}{\sqrt{a_1^2 + b_1^2 + c_1^2}}.$$

But $a_1x_1 + b_1y_1 + c_1z_1 = -d_1$, since the point P_1 lies on the plane $a_1x + b_1y + c_1z + d_1 = 0$. Therefore,

$$r = \frac{|d_3 - d_1|}{\sqrt{a_1^2 + b_1^2 + c_1^2}}. \tag{3-36}$$

Equation (3-36) represents the formula for the distance between two parallel planes of the form in (3-35).

Example 3 Find the distance between the planes

$$6x - 3y + 6z + 2 = 0$$

and

$$2x - y + 2z + 4 = 0.$$

The planes are parallel since $6/2 = -3/-1 = 6/2 = 3$. Multiplying the terms on each side of the second equation by 3, the set of equations becomes

$$6x - 3y + 6z + 2 = 0$$

and

$$6x - 3y + 6z + 12 = 0.$$

By equation (3-36), the distance r between the two parallel planes is given as

$$r = \frac{|12 - 2|}{\sqrt{(6)^2 + (-3)^2 + (6)^2}} = 10/9; \text{ that is, } 10/9 \text{ units.}$$

Exercises

1. Find the distance between P_1: $(0, -5, 2)$ and the plane $x + 2y + z - 4 = 0$.
2. Find the distance between the origin and the plane $x - 2y - 2z - 3 = 0$.
3. Determine d such that the distance between P_1: $(4, 0, 1)$ and the plane $2x + y - 2z + d = 0$ is 3.
4. Find the distance between P_1: $(0, 0, 4)$ and the plane $2x + 2y - 3 = 0$.
5. Find the distance between the parallel planes $3x - 4y + 12z + 4 = 0$ and $3x - 4y + 12z - 22 = 0$.
6. Find the distance between the planes $x + y - 2z = 2$ and $3x + 3y - 6z = 2$.
7. If the coordinates of P satisfy the equation $x + 2y + 3z - 4 = 0$, then determine the value of d such that the coordinates of the mid-point of line segment OP satisfy the equation $x + 2y + 3z + d = 0$.
8. Determine the value of d such that the plane $2x - 2y + z + d = 0$ is tangent to the sphere $x^2 + y^2 + z^2 - 2x - 4y + 2z - 10 = 0$.
9. Determine the equation of the sphere with center at C: $(2, 2, 1)$ which is tangent to the plane $3x + 4y + 12z = 0$.

3-6 Equation of a Line

As in the case of the plane in space, there are several ways of specifying a line in space, such as giving two points on the line, or two planes through the line, or a point on the line and a set of direction numbers for the line, or by other means. It will be convenient to determine the form of an equation of a straight line by designating a point through which it passes and a vector to which it is parallel.

Let P_1: (x_1, y_1, z_1) be the point through which the line l passes and $\vec{r} = a\vec{i} + b\vec{j} + c\vec{k}$ be the vector parallel to the line (Figure 3-8). Let P: (x, y, z) be a general point on line l. Since $\overrightarrow{OP} - \overrightarrow{OP_1}$ is parallel to $\vec{r}$, it follows that

$$(\overrightarrow{OP} - \overrightarrow{OP_1}) \times \vec{r} = \vec{0}, \quad (3\text{-}37)$$

which is a vector form of the equation of the straight line l. Another vector form of the equation of the straight line is expressed by

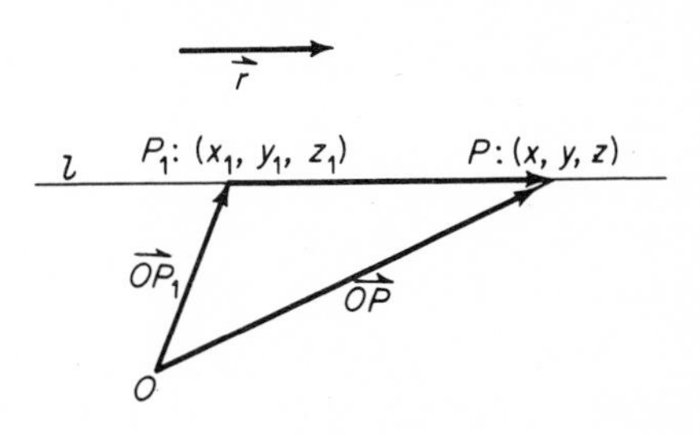

Figure 3-8

$$\overrightarrow{OP} - \overrightarrow{OP_1} = m\vec{r}, \quad (3\text{-}38)$$

where m represents any real number. Since

$$\overrightarrow{OP} = x\vec{i} + y\vec{j} + z\vec{k}, \qquad \overrightarrow{OP_1} = x_1\vec{i} + y_1\vec{j} + z_1\vec{k},$$

and

$$\overrightarrow{OP} - \overrightarrow{OP_1} = (x - x_1)\vec{i} + (y - y_1)\vec{j} + (z - z_1)\vec{k},$$

$$(x - x_1)\vec{i} + (y - y_1)\vec{j} + (z - z_1)\vec{k} = m(a\vec{i} + b\vec{j} + c\vec{k}).$$

By equating components, since $\vec{i}$, $\vec{j}$, and $\vec{k}$ are linearly independent vectors,

$$(x - x_1) = ma, \qquad (y - y_1) = mb, \qquad (z - z_1) = mc;$$

$$\begin{cases} x = x_1 + ma, \\ y = y_1 + mb, \\ z = z_1 + mc. \end{cases} \quad (3\text{-}39)$$

The equations of (3-39) represent a set of **parametric equations of a line** l with parameter m. Each point of the line corresponds to a value of the parameter. Note that $(a\colon b\colon c)$ represents a set of direction numbers for the line, since a, b, and c are the components of a vector parallel to the line. After solving for m in each equation, it follows that

$$\frac{x - x_1}{a} = \frac{y - y_1}{b} = \frac{z - z_1}{c}, \quad (3\text{-}40)$$

which represents the **point-direction number form of the equation of a line** through P_1: (x_1, y_1, z_1) with direction numbers $(a\colon b\colon c)$.

The equations of (3-40) are also called the **symmetric form of the equation of a line** or a set of **symmetric equations of a line.** Note that the symmetric form of the equation of a line is not unique, since the coordinates of an infinite number of points on the line may be used as well as an infinite number of sets of direction numbers.

If either a, b, or c is zero, the symmetric form of the equation of a straight line can still be used, provided it is designated as a special convention that, whenever a denominator in the formula is zero, the formal ratio is deleted and the numerator is set equal to zero. For example, the equation

$$\frac{x - x_1}{0} = \frac{y - y_1}{b} = \frac{z - z_1}{c}, \tag{3-41}$$

where $b \neq 0$ and $c \neq 0$, shall mean

$$x - x_1 = 0; \qquad \frac{y - y_1}{b} = \frac{z - z_1}{c}. \tag{3-42}$$

There exist several vector forms of the equation of a straight line. Another vector form depends upon the concept of a set of linearly dependent vectors. Let A: (x_1, y_1, z_1) and B: (x_2, y_2, z_2) be two distinct points. Consider P: (x, y, z) a general point on the line l (Figure 3-9). Since P lies on the line determined by A and B, then by Theorem 1-9

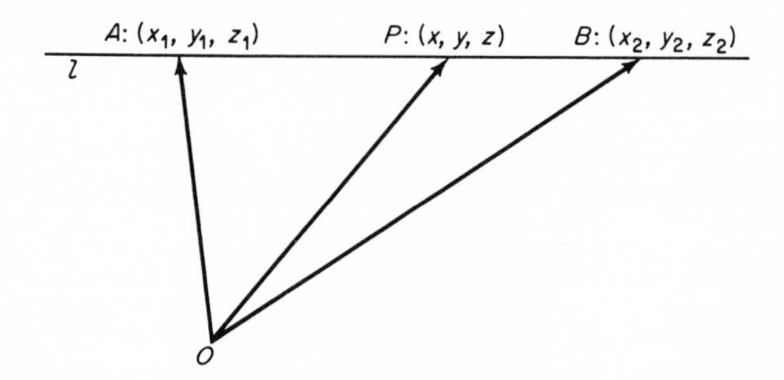

Figure 3-9

$$\overrightarrow{OP} = m\overrightarrow{OA} + (1 - m)\overrightarrow{OB} \tag{3-43}$$

represents a vector form of the equation of the line. Now, $\overrightarrow{OP} = x\vec{i} + y\vec{j} + z\vec{k}$, $\overrightarrow{OA} = x_1\vec{i} + y_1\vec{j} + z_1\vec{k}$, and $\overrightarrow{OB} = x_2\vec{i} + y_2\vec{j} + z_2\vec{k}$. Equating corresponding components after substituting in equation (3-43),

$$\begin{cases} x = mx_1 + (1 - m)x_2, \\ y = my_1 + (1 - m)y_2, \\ z = mz_1 + (1 - m)z_2. \end{cases} \tag{3-44}$$

The equations of (3-44) are another form of a set of **parametric equations of a line** through A and B with parameter m. Each point of the line corresponds to a value of the parameter. Solving for m in each equation of (3-44), it follows that

$$\frac{x - x_2}{x_1 - x_2} = \frac{y - y_2}{y_1 - y_2} = \frac{z - z_2}{z_1 - z_2}, \tag{3-45}$$

which represents the **two-point form of the equation of a line** through $A: (x_1, y_1, z_1)$ and $B: (x_2, y_2, z_2)$. Note that the two-point form of the equation of a straight line on a plane is a special case of (3-45).

Example 1 Determine a set of symmetric equations of the line through $P_1: (4, 1, 5)$ and parallel to $\vec{r} = 2\vec{i} - 2\vec{j} + 3\vec{k}$.

The components of $\vec{r}$ provide a set of direction numbers for the line: (2: −2: 3). The equations of (3-40) where $x_1 = 4$, $y_1 = 1$, and $z_1 = 5$ provide the symmetric equations of the line:

$$\frac{x - 4}{2} = \frac{y - 1}{-2} = \frac{z - 5}{3}.$$

Example 2 Determine a set of parametric equations of the line in Example 1.

By the equations of (3-39), a set of parametric equations of the line is

$$\begin{cases} x = 4 + 2m, \\ y = 1 - 2m, \\ z = 5 + 3m. \end{cases}$$

Example 3 Determine a vector form of the equation of the line through A: (2, 3, 4) and B: (−1, 2, 1). Use the vector form to determine a set of symmetric equations of the line. Compare the results with those obtained by using the equations of (3-45).

Let $P: (x, y, z)$ be any point on the line through A and B. Then

$$\overrightarrow{OP} = m\overrightarrow{OA} + (1 - m)\overrightarrow{OB}.$$

Since $\overrightarrow{OP} = x\vec{i} + y\vec{j} + z\vec{k}$, $\overrightarrow{OA} = 2\vec{i} + 3\vec{j} + 4\vec{k}$, and $\overrightarrow{OB} = -\vec{i} + 2\vec{j} + \vec{k}$,

$$\begin{aligned} x\vec{i} + y\vec{j} + z\vec{k} &= 2m\vec{i} + 3m\vec{j} + 4m\vec{k} - (1 - m)\vec{i} + 2(1 - m)\vec{j} \\ &\quad + (1 - m)\vec{k} \\ &= (3m - 1)\vec{i} + (m + 2)\vec{j} + (3m + 1)\vec{k}; \end{aligned}$$

that is,

$$(x - 3m + 1)\vec{i} + (y - m - 2)\vec{j} + (z - 3m - 1)\vec{k} = \vec{0},$$

which represents a vector form of the equation of the line.

Since $\vec{i}$, $\vec{j}$, and $\vec{k}$ are linearly independent vectors,

$$\begin{cases} x - 3m + 1 = 0, \\ y - m - 2 = 0, \\ z - 3m - 1 = 0; \end{cases}$$

that is,

$$\begin{cases} \dfrac{x+1}{3} = m, \\ \dfrac{y-2}{1} = m, \\ \dfrac{z-1}{3} = m. \end{cases}$$

Hence,

$$\frac{x+1}{3} = \frac{y-2}{1} = \frac{z-1}{3}$$

is a set of symmetric equations of the line through A and B.

By the equations of (3-45) with $(x_1, y_1, z_1) = (2, 3, 4)$ and $(x_2, y_2, z_2) = (-1, 2, 1)$,

$$\frac{x-(-1)}{2-(-1)} = \frac{y-2}{3-2} = \frac{z-1}{4-1};$$

that is,

$$\frac{x+1}{3} = \frac{y-2}{1} = \frac{z-1}{3},$$

which agrees with the results obtained using the vector form of the equation of the line.

Example 4 Determine a set of symmetric equations of the line through the origin and $P_1: (x_1, y_1, z_1)$.

Let $(x_2, y_2, z_2) = (0, 0, 0)$ in the equations of (3-45). Then

$$\frac{x}{x_1} = \frac{y}{y_1} = \frac{z}{z_1}$$

represents a set of symmetric equations of the line through the origin and $P_1: (x_1, y_1, z_1)$.

Since an equation such as $ax + by + cz + d = 0$ represents a plane, two such equations considered simultaneously represent two planes which will intersect in a straight line, if they are not parallel. The condition that the two planes be parallel is that the coefficients of x, y, z in their equations be proportional. Therefore, except when $a_1/a_2 = b_1/b_2 = c_1/c_2$, the set of two equations

$$\begin{cases} a_1x + b_1y + c_1z + d_1 = 0, \\ a_2x + b_2y + c_2z + d_2 = 0, \end{cases} \tag{3-46}$$

taken simultaneously represents a line, and is called the **general form of the equation of a line.**

Many pairs of planes may be passed through the same line. Therefore, a line may be represented by any one of infinitely many pairs of planes through the line.

To determine a set of symmetric equations of a line by means of a pair of equations for the planes, first locate the coordinates of two of the **piercing points;** that is, the points of intersection of the line with two of the following three planes: xy-plane, xz-plane, or yz-plane. This can be done by letting x, y, or z be zero and solving the resulting two equations simultaneously.

A set of symmetric equations of the line may then be determined by using (3-45).

Example 5 Find a set of symmetric equations of the line determined by the equations

$$\begin{cases} 3x - y + z = 8, \\ 2x + y + 4z = 2. \end{cases}$$

If $z = 0$, then the two equations

$$\begin{cases} 3x - y = 8, \\ 2x + y = 2, \end{cases}$$

when solved simultaneously, determine the piercing point A: $(2, -2, 0)$ of the xy-plane. If $x = 0$, then the two equations

$$\begin{cases} -y + z = 8, \\ y + 4z = 2, \end{cases}$$

when solved simultaneously, determine the piercing point B: $(0, -6, 2)$ of the yz-plane. Now $\overrightarrow{BA} = 2\vec{i} + 4\vec{j} - 2\vec{k}$. Therefore $(2\!:4\!:-2)$ is a set of direction numbers for the line BA. Hence a set of symmetric equations of line BA is

$$\frac{x-2}{2} = \frac{y+2}{4} = \frac{z}{-2}.$$

Example 6 Determine a set of direction numbers for the line determined by the planes

$$\begin{cases} a_1x + b_1y + c_1z + d_1 = 0, \\ a_2x + b_2y + c_2z + d_2 = 0. \end{cases}$$

The line determined by the two planes is perpendicular to the vectors normal to the planes; that is, $a_1\vec{i} + b_1\vec{j} + c_1\vec{k}$ and $a_2\vec{i} + b_2\vec{j} + c_2\vec{k}$. A position vector parallel to the line is given by Theorem 2-15 in the expression

$$\begin{vmatrix} \vec{i} & \vec{j} & \vec{k} \\ a_1 & b_1 & c_1 \\ a_2 & b_2 & c_2 \end{vmatrix}; \text{ that is,}$$

$$\begin{vmatrix} b_1 & c_1 \\ b_2 & c_2 \end{vmatrix}\vec{i} + \begin{vmatrix} c_1 & a_1 \\ c_2 & a_2 \end{vmatrix}\vec{j} + \begin{vmatrix} a_1 & b_1 \\ a_2 & b_2 \end{vmatrix}\vec{k}.$$

The components of this vector comprise a set of direction numbers for the line. Hence,

$$\left(\begin{vmatrix} b_1 & c_1 \\ b_2 & c_2 \end{vmatrix} : \begin{vmatrix} c_1 & a_1 \\ c_2 & a_2 \end{vmatrix} : \begin{vmatrix} a_1 & b_1 \\ a_2 & b_2 \end{vmatrix}\right)$$

is a set of direction numbers for the line determined by the planes

$$\begin{cases} a_1x + b_1y + c_1z + d_1 = 0, \\ a_2x + b_2y + c_2z + d_2 = 0. \end{cases}$$

Exercises

1. Determine a set of parametric equations of the line through P_1: (4, 5, 2) and parallel to $\vec{r} = 2\vec{i} - 3\vec{j} + \vec{k}$.
2. Determine a set of symmetric equations of the line in Exercise 1.
3. Use the concept of linear dependence of vectors to determine a set of symmetric equations of the line through A: (1, 2, 0) and B: (4, 3, −2).
4. Determine a set of parametric equations of the line through the origin and P_1: (3, 5, −1).
5. Determine a set of symmetric equations of the line in Exercise 4.
6. Given the line $x = 2 + 4m$, $y = 2$, and $z = 3 - 3m$, find **(a)** a set of direction numbers; **(b)** a set of direction cosines; **(c)** three points on the line.
7. Find a set of parametric equations of the line through A: (4, 1, 3) and B: (1, 1, 2).
8. Find a set of symmetric equations of the line through A: (1, 1, −5) and having a set of direction numbers (4: 2: 3).
9. Find a set of symmetric equations of the line through A: (3, −1, 4) and parallel to the line
$$\frac{x+1}{3} = \frac{y}{5} = \frac{z-7}{2}.$$
10. Find a set of parametric equations of the line through A: (5, 1, 2) and perpendicular to the plane $4x + 2y + 5z - 18 = 0$.
11. Determine a set of direction cosines of the line
$$\frac{x-1}{2} = \frac{y+2}{-2} = z - 2.$$
12. Determine t if the line
$$\frac{x+1}{3} = \frac{y-2}{6} = \frac{z-3}{4}$$
is parallel to the plane $2x + 3y - tz + 7 = 0$.

13. Determine a set of direction cosines of the line common to the planes $2x - y + z + 3 = 0$ and $5x + y - z + 4 = 0$.

14. Find a set of symmetric equations of the line determined by the planes $x - y + z = 8$ and $2x + y - z = 1$.

15. Determine the coordinates of the point of intersection of the line through A: $(-2, 3, 7)$ and B: $(6, -1, 2)$, and the xy-plane.

16. Determine the coordinates of the point of intersection of the line through A: $(1, 1, 1)$ and B: $(3, 2, 1)$, and the plane $x - 3y = 0$.

17. Show that a vector parallel to the line determined by $3x - y - 5 = 0$ and $4x - z - 9 = 0$ is perpendicular to a vector parallel to the line determined by $y + z = 0$ and $x - y - 1 = 0$.

18. Show that the line determined by $5x + y - 3z + 1 = 0$ and $3x - 6y - 4z + 15 = 0$ is parallel to the line determined by $x - y - z = 0$ and $7x + 2y - 4z - 3 = 0$.

19. Find the equation of the plane which passes through the points A: $(3, 2, -1)$ and B: $(2, 5, 0)$, and is parallel to the line

$$\frac{x-2}{3} = \frac{y-1}{2} = \frac{z}{-1}.$$

20. Find the equation of the plane passing through the two parallel lines

$$\frac{x-x_0}{\cos\alpha} = \frac{y-y_0}{\cos\beta} = \frac{z-z_0}{\cos\gamma} \quad \text{and} \quad \frac{x-x_1}{\cos\alpha} = \frac{y-y_1}{\cos\beta} = \frac{z-z_1}{\cos\gamma}.$$

3-7 Skew Lines

Two nonintersecting, nonparallel lines in space are called skew lines. Consider the equations of two skew lines

$$\begin{aligned} \frac{x-x_0}{\cos\alpha_0} &= \frac{y-y_0}{\cos\beta_0} = \frac{z-z_0}{\cos\gamma_0}, \\ \frac{x-x_1}{\cos\alpha_1} &= \frac{y-y_1}{\cos\beta_1} = \frac{z-z_1}{\cos\gamma_1}, \end{aligned} \tag{3-47}$$

where $(\cos\alpha_i : \cos\beta_i : \cos\gamma_i)$ for $i = 0, 1$ represent sets of direction cosines for the lines. The angle θ between the skew lines of (3-47) will be defined as the angle between two vectors

$$\begin{aligned} \vec{v}_0 &= \cos\alpha_0\vec{i} + \cos\beta_0\vec{j} + \cos\gamma_0\vec{k}, \\ \vec{v}_1 &= \cos\alpha_1\vec{i} + \cos\beta_1\vec{j} + \cos\gamma_1\vec{k}, \end{aligned} \tag{3-48}$$

with associated directions. Therefore,

$$\cos\theta = \pm\frac{\vec{v}_0\cdot\vec{v}_1}{|\vec{v}_0||\vec{v}_1|}; \tag{3-49}$$

that is,

$$\cos\theta = \pm(\cos\alpha_0\cos\alpha_1 + \cos\beta_0\cos\beta_1 + \cos\gamma_0\cos\gamma_1). \tag{3-50}$$

Note that since $\sin^2\theta = 1 - \cos^2\theta$, we may write the sine of the angle between two skew lines in the useful form

$$\sin^2\theta = (\cos^2\alpha_0 + \cos^2\beta_0 + \cos^2\gamma_0)(\cos^2\alpha_1 + \cos^2\beta_1 + \cos^2\gamma_1) - (\cos\alpha_0\cos\alpha_1 + \cos\beta_0\cos\beta_1 + \cos\gamma_0\cos\gamma_1)^2;$$

that is,

$$\begin{aligned}\sin^2\theta = &(\cos\beta_0\cos\gamma_1 - \cos\beta_1\cos\gamma_0)^2\\ &+ (\cos\gamma_0\cos\alpha_1 - \cos\gamma_1\cos\alpha_0)^2\\ &+ (\cos\alpha_0\cos\beta_1 - \cos\alpha_1\cos\beta_0)^2.\end{aligned} \tag{3-51}$$

Making use of determinants,

$$\sin^2\theta = \begin{vmatrix}\cos\beta_0 & \cos\gamma_0\\ \cos\beta_1 & \cos\gamma_1\end{vmatrix}^2 + \begin{vmatrix}\cos\gamma_0 & \cos\alpha_0\\ \cos\gamma_1 & \cos\alpha_1\end{vmatrix}^2 + \begin{vmatrix}\cos\alpha_0 & \cos\beta_0\\ \cos\alpha_1 & \cos\beta_1\end{vmatrix}^2. \tag{3-52}$$

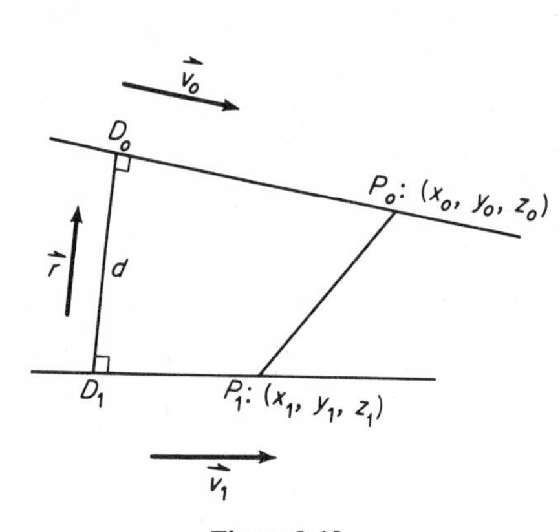

Figure 3-10

In order to determine the distance d between the two skew lines of (3-47), that is, the length of the common perpendicular, note that d in Figure 3-10 is equal to the magnitude of projection of $\overrightarrow{P_0P_1}$ on a vector $\vec{r}$ whose direction is that of the line D_0D_1. Now,

$$\vec{r} = \overrightarrow{v_0} \times \overrightarrow{v_1}; \tag{3-53}$$

that is,

$$\vec{r} = \begin{vmatrix}\cos\beta_0 & \cos\gamma_0\\ \cos\beta_1 & \cos\gamma_1\end{vmatrix}\vec{i} + \begin{vmatrix}\cos\gamma_0 & \cos\alpha_0\\ \cos\gamma_1 & \cos\alpha_1\end{vmatrix}\vec{j} + \begin{vmatrix}\cos\alpha_0 & \cos\beta_0\\ \cos\alpha_1 & \cos\beta_1\end{vmatrix}\vec{k}, \tag{3-54}$$

and $\overrightarrow{P_0P_1} = (x_1 - x_0)\vec{i} + (y_1 - y_0)\vec{j} + (z_1 - z_0)\vec{k}$. The distance d is given by the expression

$$d = \frac{|\overrightarrow{P_0P_1}\cdot\vec{r}\,|}{|\vec{r}\,|}. \tag{3-55}$$

Hence,

$$d = \pm\frac{(x_1 - x_0)\begin{vmatrix}\cos\beta_0 & \cos\gamma_0\\ \cos\beta_1 & \cos\gamma_1\end{vmatrix} + (y_1 - y_0)\begin{vmatrix}\cos\gamma_0 & \cos\alpha_0\\ \cos\gamma_1 & \cos\alpha_1\end{vmatrix} + (z_1 - z_0)\begin{vmatrix}\cos\alpha_0 & \cos\beta_0\\ \cos\alpha_1 & \cos\beta_1\end{vmatrix}}{\sqrt{\begin{vmatrix}\cos\beta_0 & \cos\gamma_0\\ \cos\beta_1 & \cos\gamma_1\end{vmatrix}^2 + \begin{vmatrix}\cos\gamma_0 & \cos\alpha_0\\ \cos\gamma_1 & \cos\alpha_1\end{vmatrix}^2 + \begin{vmatrix}\cos\alpha_0 & \cos\beta_0\\ \cos\alpha_1 & \cos\beta_1\end{vmatrix}^2}}, \tag{3-56}$$

where the $\pm$ sign is chosen so that $d > 0$. By (3-52),

$$d = \pm\frac{1}{\sin\theta}\begin{vmatrix} x_1 - x_0 & y_1 - y_0 & z_1 - z_0 \\ \cos\alpha_0 & \cos\beta_0 & \cos\gamma_0 \\ \cos\alpha_1 & \cos\beta_1 & \cos\gamma_1 \end{vmatrix}. \tag{3-57}$$

If the skew lines are given in the form

$$\begin{aligned} \frac{x - x_0}{l_0} &= \frac{y - y_0}{m_0} = \frac{z - z_0}{n_0}, \\ \frac{x - x_1}{l_1} &= \frac{y - y_1}{m_1} = \frac{z - z_1}{n_1}, \end{aligned} \tag{3-58}$$

where $(l_i : m_i : n_i)$ for $i = 0, 1$ are sets of direction numbers, then it can be shown that

$$d = \pm\frac{\begin{vmatrix} x_1 - x_0 & y_1 - y_0 & z_1 - z_0 \\ l_0 & m_0 & n_0 \\ l_1 & m_1 & n_1 \end{vmatrix}}{\sqrt{\begin{vmatrix} m_0 & n_0 \\ m_1 & n_1 \end{vmatrix}^2 + \begin{vmatrix} n_0 & l_0 \\ n_1 & l_1 \end{vmatrix}^2 + \begin{vmatrix} l_0 & m_0 \\ l_1 & m_1 \end{vmatrix}^2}}. \tag{3-59}$$

It immediately follows that a necessary and sufficient condition for two lines of the form (3-58) to be concurrent and distinct is

$$\begin{vmatrix} x_1 - x_0 & y_1 - y_0 & z_1 - z_0 \\ l_0 & m_0 & n_0 \\ l_1 & m_1 & n_1 \end{vmatrix} = 0, \tag{3-60}$$

provided l_0, m_0, n_0 are not identical multiples of l_1, m_1, n_1, respectively.

In order to find the equation of the common perpendicular it will be convenient to determine the equations of two planes containing the line D_0D_1 of Figure 3-10. A vector form of the equation of one plane with general point P: (x, y, z) is expressed by

$$\overrightarrow{P_0P} \cdot \vec{v}_0 \times \vec{r} = 0. \tag{3-61}$$

Similarly, a vector form of the equation of a second plane containing the line D_0D_1 is expressed by

$$\overrightarrow{P_1P} \cdot \vec{v}_1 \times \vec{r} = 0. \tag{3-62}$$

The line D_0D_1 is defined by equations (3-61) and (3-62) taken simultaneously. These equations may be written in the determinant forms

$$\begin{vmatrix} x - x_0 & y - y_0 & z - z_0 \\ l_0 & m_0 & n_0 \\ m_0n_1 - m_1n_0 & n_0l_1 - n_1l_0 & l_0m_1 - l_1m_0 \end{vmatrix} = 0, \tag{3-63}$$

and

$$\begin{vmatrix} x - x_1 & y - y_1 & z - z_1 \\ l_1 & m_1 & n_1 \\ m_0n_1 - m_1n_0 & n_0l_1 - n_1l_0 & l_0m_1 - l_1m_0 \end{vmatrix} = 0. \tag{3-64}$$

Example 1 Determine the shortest distance between the skew lines L_0 and L_1:

$$(L_0) \quad \frac{x-1}{2} = \frac{y}{3} = \frac{z+1}{1},$$

$$(L_1) \quad \frac{x}{3} = \frac{y-3}{4} = \frac{z-1}{2}.$$

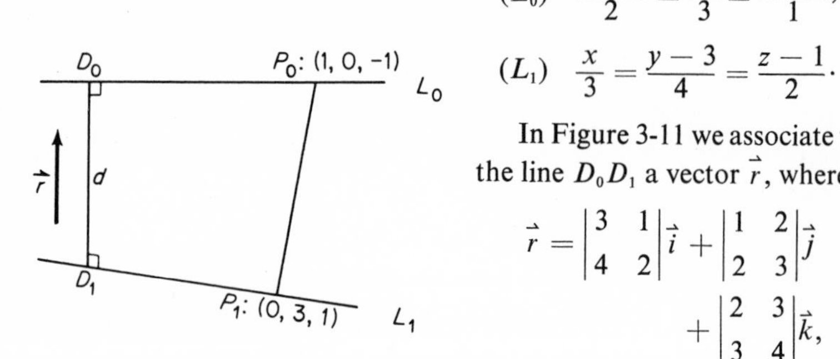

Figure 3-11

In Figure 3-11 we associate with the line D_0D_1 a vector $\vec{r}$, where

$$\vec{r} = \begin{vmatrix} 3 & 1 \\ 4 & 2 \end{vmatrix} \vec{i} + \begin{vmatrix} 1 & 2 \\ 2 & 3 \end{vmatrix} \vec{j} + \begin{vmatrix} 2 & 3 \\ 3 & 4 \end{vmatrix} \vec{k},$$

$$= 2\vec{i} - \vec{j} - \vec{k}.$$

In addition, $\overrightarrow{P_0P_1} = -\vec{i} + 3\vec{j} + 2\vec{k}$. The distance d is given by the magnitude of the projection of $\overrightarrow{P_0P_1}$ on $\vec{r}$. Hence,

$$d = \frac{|\overrightarrow{P_0P_1} \cdot \vec{r}|}{|\vec{r}|}$$

$$= \frac{|(-1)(2) + (3)(-1) + (2)(-1)|}{\sqrt{2^2 + (-1)^2 + (-1)^2}}$$

$$= \frac{7\sqrt{6}}{6}; \text{ that is, } \frac{7\sqrt{6}}{6} \text{ units.}$$

Example 2 Determine the equation of the line D_0D_1 in Example 1.

Associate with lines L_0 and L_1 two vectors v_0 and v_1, where

$$\vec{v_0} = 2\vec{i} + 3\vec{j} + \vec{k},$$

$$\vec{v_1} = 3\vec{i} + 4\vec{j} + 2\vec{k}.$$

Then the equation of two distinct planes containing line D_0D_1 is given by the equations

$$\overrightarrow{P_0P} \cdot \vec{v_0} \times \vec{r} = 0,$$

and

$$\overrightarrow{P_1P} \cdot \vec{v_1} \times \vec{r} = 0,$$

where P represents the general point (x, y, z) in each plane. The equations of these planes in terms of the coordinates of P_0 and P_1 and the direction numbers of lines L_0 and L_1 may be expressed by

$$\begin{vmatrix} x-1 & y & z+1 \\ 2 & 3 & 1 \\ 2 & -1 & -1 \end{vmatrix} = 0,$$

and

$$\begin{vmatrix} x & y-3 & z-1 \\ 3 & 4 & 2 \\ 2 & -1 & -1 \end{vmatrix} = 0;$$

that is,

$$x - 2y + 4z + 3 = 0,$$

and

$$2x - 7y + 11z + 10 = 0.$$

Taken simultaneously, the equations of the two planes represent the equation of the common perpendicular to the skew lines L_0 and L_1.

Exercises

1. Find the acute angle between the given lines:

(a) $\frac{x-1}{1} = \frac{y}{2} = \frac{z-5}{-2}$ and $\frac{x+6}{3} = \frac{y-2}{-4} = \frac{z}{5}$;

(b) $\frac{x-1}{2} = \frac{y+1}{-3} = \frac{z}{4}$ and $\frac{x-3}{1} = \frac{y+6}{2} = \frac{z+2}{1}$.

2. Determine the distance between the skew lines $x = 2 + 2m$, $y = 1 + m$, $z = 2$, and $x = 6 - 4m$, $y = -2 - m$, $z = 1 + 3m$.

3. Find the common perpendicular of the lines in Exercise 2.

4. Find the distance between any diagonal of a cube of side s and an edge skew to it.

5. Show that the lines $x = -2 + m$, $y = 4 - m$, $z = -2 + 2m$ and $x = 1 + 2m$, $y = 3$, $z = 3 + 3m$ are concurrent. Determine the equation of the plane defined by the lines.

6. Determine the general equation of the plane containing the line

$$\frac{x - x_0}{l} = \frac{y - y_0}{m} = \frac{z - z_0}{n}$$

and perpendicular to the plane $ax + by + cz + d = 0$.

3-8 Distance Between a Point and a Line

Consider a line L whose equation is of the form

$$\frac{x - x_0}{\cos\alpha} = \frac{y - y_0}{\cos\beta} = \frac{z - z_0}{\cos\gamma},$$

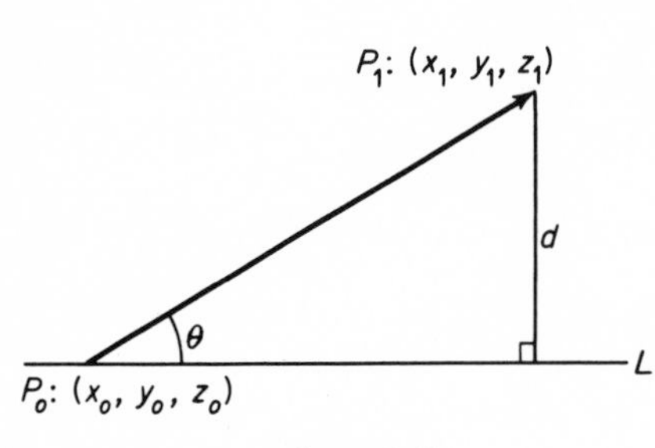

Figure 3-12

where $(\cos\alpha : \cos\beta : \cos\gamma)$ represents a set of direction cosines for the line, and a point P_1: (x_1, y_1, z_1) not on L (Figure 3-12). Now, the distance d between the point P_1 and the line L is given by the equation

$$d = |\overrightarrow{P_0P_1}| \sin\theta, \tag{3-65}$$

and

$$d^2 = |\overrightarrow{P_0P_1}|^2 \sin^2\theta, \tag{3-66}$$

where θ is the angle between the line L and the line P_0P_1. A unit vector parallel to the line P_0P_1 is given by

$$\frac{x_1 - x_0}{|\overrightarrow{P_0P_1}|}\vec{i} + \frac{y_1 - y_0}{|\overrightarrow{P_0P_1}|}\vec{j} + \frac{z_1 - z_0}{|\overrightarrow{P_0P_1}|}\vec{k},$$

while a unit vector parallel to the line L is given by

$$\cos\alpha\vec{i} + \cos\beta\vec{j} + \cos\gamma\vec{k}.$$

Hence, by equation (3-52),

$$\sin^2\theta = \begin{vmatrix} \dfrac{y_1 - y_0}{|\overrightarrow{P_0P_1}|} & \dfrac{z_1 - z_0}{|\overrightarrow{P_0P_1}|} \\ \cos\beta & \cos\gamma \end{vmatrix}^2 + \begin{vmatrix} \dfrac{z_1 - z_0}{|\overrightarrow{P_0P_1}|} & \dfrac{x_1 - x_0}{|\overrightarrow{P_0P_1}|} \\ \cos\gamma & \cos\alpha \end{vmatrix}^2 + \begin{vmatrix} \dfrac{x_1 - x_0}{|\overrightarrow{P_0P_1}|} & \dfrac{y_1 - y_0}{|\overrightarrow{P_0P_1}|} \\ \cos\alpha & \cos\beta \end{vmatrix}^2. \tag{3-67}$$

Therefore, since $d^2 = |\overrightarrow{P_0P_1}|^2 \sin^2\theta$, the distance d between the given point P_1 and the given line L is expressed by the relationship

$$d^2 = \begin{vmatrix} y_1 - y_0 & z_1 - z_0 \\ \cos\beta & \cos\gamma \end{vmatrix}^2 + \begin{vmatrix} z_1 - z_0 & x_1 - x_0 \\ \cos\gamma & \cos\alpha \end{vmatrix}^2 + \begin{vmatrix} x_1 - x_0 & y_1 - y_0 \\ \cos\alpha & \cos\beta \end{vmatrix}^2. \tag{3-68}$$

Example 1 Find the distance between P_1: $(2, 3, 1)$ and the line

$$\frac{x - 1}{1} = \frac{y + 2}{2} = \frac{z - 2}{-2}.$$

By equation (3-68), where $(x_1, y_1, z_1) = (2, 3, 1)$, $(x_0, y_0, z_0) = (1, -2, 2)$, and $(\cos\alpha : \cos\beta : \cos\gamma) = (\frac{1}{3} : \frac{2}{3} : -\frac{2}{3})$,

$$d^2 = \begin{vmatrix} 5 & -1 \\ \frac{2}{3} & -\frac{2}{3} \end{vmatrix}^2 + \begin{vmatrix} -1 & 1 \\ -\frac{2}{3} & \frac{1}{3} \end{vmatrix}^2 + \begin{vmatrix} 1 & 5 \\ \frac{1}{3} & \frac{2}{3} \end{vmatrix}^2$$

$$= \tfrac{64}{9} + \tfrac{1}{9} + \tfrac{9}{9} = \tfrac{74}{9}.$$

Therefore,

$$d = \frac{\sqrt{74}}{3}; \quad \text{that is,} \quad \frac{\sqrt{74}}{3} \text{ units.}$$

Example 2 Find a formula for the distance between the origin and any line

$$\frac{x - x_0}{\cos\alpha} = \frac{y - y_0}{\cos\beta} = \frac{z - z_0}{\cos\gamma},$$

where $(\cos\alpha : \cos\beta : \cos\gamma)$ represents a set of direction cosines for the line.

By equation (3-68), where $(x_1, y_1, z_1) = (0, 0, 0)$, it follows that

$$d^2 = \begin{vmatrix} -y_0 & -z_0 \\ \cos\beta & \cos\gamma \end{vmatrix}^2 + \begin{vmatrix} -z_0 & -x_0 \\ \cos\gamma & \cos\alpha \end{vmatrix}^2 + \begin{vmatrix} -x_0 & -y_0 \\ \cos\alpha & \cos\beta \end{vmatrix}^2.$$

Hence,

$$d = \sqrt{\begin{vmatrix} y_0 & z_0 \\ \cos\beta & \cos\gamma \end{vmatrix}^2 + \begin{vmatrix} z_0 & x_0 \\ \cos\gamma & \cos\alpha \end{vmatrix}^2 + \begin{vmatrix} x_0 & y_0 \\ \cos\alpha & \cos\beta \end{vmatrix}^2} \qquad (3\text{-}69)$$

represents the formula for the distance between the origin and the given line.

Exercises

1. Find the distance between P_1: $(2, 5, -1)$ and the line through P_0: $(4, 5, 3)$ with direction numbers $(3 : -6 : -2)$.
2. Find the distance between P_1: $(2, -3, -1)$ and the line through P_0: $(3, -5, -2)$ which makes equal angles with the positive halves of the axes.
3. Find the distance between the vertex of a cube of side s and a diagonal of the cube which does not contain that vertex.

Bibliography for Reference

Barnett, Raymond A., and John N. Fujii, *Vectors*. New York: John Wiley & Sons, Inc., 1963.

Copeland, Arthur H., *Geometry, Algebra,* and *Trigonometry by Vector Methods*. New York: The Macmillan Company, 1962.

Gibbs, J. Willard, *Vector Analysis*. New Haven: Yale University Press, 1922.

Glicksman, Abraham, *Vectors In Three Dimensional Geometry*. Washington, D. C.: National Council of Teachers of Mathematics, 1961.

Halmos, Paul R., *Finite-Dimensional Vector Spaces*. Princeton, New Jersey: D. Van Nostrand Co., Inc., 1958.

Hardy, A. S., *Elements of Quaternions*. Boston: Ginn and Company, 1881.

Hay, G. E., *Vector and Tensor Analysis*. New York: Dover Publications, Inc., 1953.

Jaeger, Arno, *Introduction to Analytic Geometry and Linear Algebra*. New York: Holt, Rinehart and Winston, Inc., 1960.

Kelland, P., and P. G. Tait, *Introduction to Quaternions*. London: Macmillan and Co., Ltd., 1873.

Lass, H., *Vector and Tensor Analysis*. New York: McGraw-Hill Book Company, 1950.

Maxwell, E. A., *Coordinate Geometry with Vectors and Tensors*. London: Oxford University Press, 1958.

Meserve, Bruce E., Anthony J. Pettofrezzo, and Dorothy T. Meserve, *Principles of Advanced Mathematics*. Syracuse: The L. W. Singer Company, 1964.

Paige, Lowell J., and J. Dean Swift, *Elements of Linear Algebra*. Boston: Ginn and Company, 1961.

Prenowitz, Walter, "Geometric Vector Analysis and the Concept of Vector Space," *Twenty-Third Yearbook: Insights Into Modern Mathematics*. Washington, D. C.: National Council of Teachers of Mathematics, 1957.

Robinson, Gilbert de B., *Vector Geometry*. Boston: Allyn and Bacon, Inc., 1962.

Schuster, Seymour, *Elementary Vector Geometry*. New York: John Wiley & Sons, Inc., 1962.

Schwartz, Manuel, Simon Green, and W. A. Rutledge, *Vector Analysis*. New York: Harper & Row, Publishers, 1960.

Weatherburn, C. E., *Elementary Vector Analysis*. London: G. Bell and Sons, Ltd., 1935.

Wexler, Charles, *Analytic Geometry: A Vector Approach*. Reading, Massachusetts: Addison-Wesley Publishing Company, Inc., 1962.

Answers For Odd-Numbered Exercises

Chapter 1—Elementary Operations

1-1 Scalars and Vectors

1. Scalar quantity.

3. Scalar quantity.

5. Vector quantity.

1-2 Equality of Vectors

1. Not equal.

3. Equal.

5. Not equal.

7.

P

9.

P

11.

P

1-3 Vector Addition and Subtraction

1. **(a)** $\overrightarrow{AD}$; **(b)** $\vec{0}$.

3.

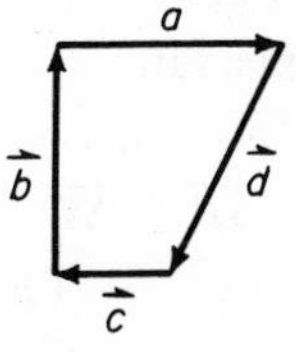

$\vec{a}$ $\vec{b}$ $\vec{c}$ $\vec{d}$

5.
$$\begin{aligned}(\vec{a} + \vec{b}) + \vec{c} &= \vec{a} + (\vec{b} + \vec{c}) \quad \text{(Theorem 1-2)}\\ &= \vec{a} + (\vec{c} + \vec{b}) \quad \text{(Theorem 1-1)}\\ &= (\vec{a} + \vec{c}) + \vec{b} \quad \text{(Theorem 1-2)}\\ &= (\vec{c} + \vec{a}) + \vec{b}. \quad \text{(Theorem 1-1)}\end{aligned}$$

7. $\overrightarrow{AB} = \overrightarrow{DC}$; that is, two opposite sides of the quadrilateral are equal and parallel. Hence $ABCD$ is a parallelogram.

9. **(a)** $\vec{a}, \vec{b}, \vec{c}, \vec{a}+\vec{b}, \vec{a}+\vec{c}, \vec{b}+\vec{c}, \vec{a}+\vec{b}+\vec{c}$.
(b) $\vec{a}+(\vec{b}+\vec{c})+(\vec{a}+\vec{b}+\vec{c}) = \vec{b}+\vec{c}+(\vec{a}+\vec{b})+(\vec{a}+\vec{c})$.
There are also other correct answers.

1-4 Multiplication of a Vector by a Scalar

1. **(a)** $3\overrightarrow{AB}$; **(b)** $2\overrightarrow{BA}$.

3.

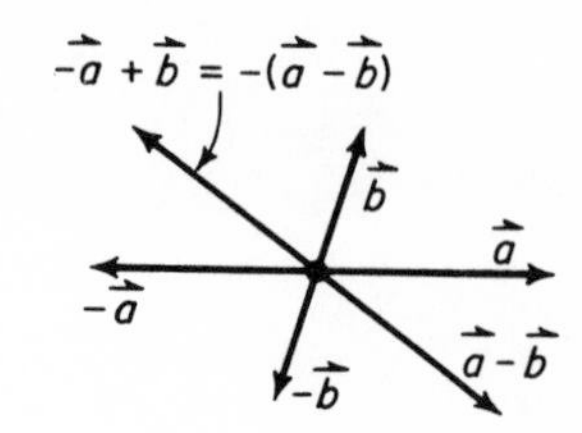

5. Let $\vec{c}$ and $\vec{d}$ represent the adjacent sides of the parallelogram. Assume $|\vec{a}| \geq |\vec{b}|$. Then $\vec{a} = \vec{c}+\vec{d}$ and $\vec{b} = \vec{c}-\vec{d}$. Therefore, $2\vec{c} = \vec{a}+\vec{b}$ and $\vec{c} = \frac{1}{2}(\vec{a}+\vec{b})$; $2\vec{d} = \vec{a}-\vec{b}$ and $\vec{d} = \frac{1}{2}(\vec{a}-\vec{b})$. Construct a parallelogram with sides $\vec{c}$ and $\vec{d}$.

7. Let $ABCD$ be any trapezoid with bases AB and DC; that is, $\overrightarrow{AB}$ is parallel to $\overrightarrow{DC}$. Let E and F be the mid-points of sides AD and BC, respectively; that is, line segment EF is the median of the trapezoid. Then,

$$\begin{aligned}\overrightarrow{EF} &= \overrightarrow{EA}+\overrightarrow{AB}+\overrightarrow{BF}\\ &= \tfrac{1}{2}\overrightarrow{DA}+\overrightarrow{AB}+\tfrac{1}{2}\overrightarrow{BC}\\ &= \tfrac{1}{2}\overrightarrow{AB}+\tfrac{1}{2}(\overrightarrow{DA}+\overrightarrow{AB}+\overrightarrow{BC})\\ &= \tfrac{1}{2}\overrightarrow{AB}+\tfrac{1}{2}\overrightarrow{DC}\\ &= \tfrac{1}{2}(\overrightarrow{AB}+\overrightarrow{DC}).\end{aligned}$$

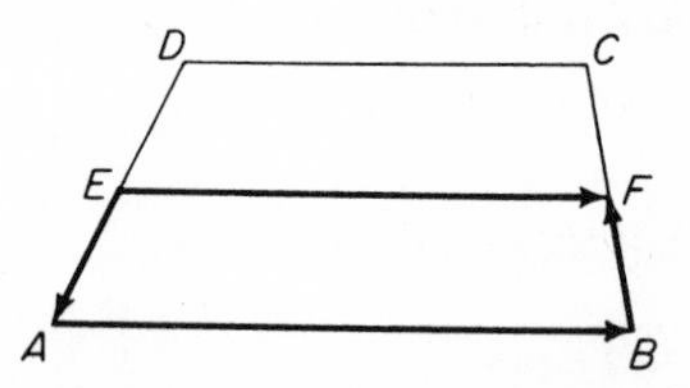

Since $\overrightarrow{AB}$ is parallel to $\overrightarrow{DC}$, then $\overrightarrow{EF}$ is parallel to both $\overrightarrow{AB}$ and $\overrightarrow{DC}$. Furthermore, $|\overrightarrow{EF}| = \frac{1}{2}|\overrightarrow{AB}+\overrightarrow{DC}| = \frac{1}{2}|\overrightarrow{AB}| + \frac{1}{2}|\overrightarrow{DC}|$. Therefore line segment EF is parallel to the bases and equal to one-half their sum.

9. Let M, N, R, and S divide sides AB, BC, CD, and DA of a parallelogram in the same ratio k to $1-k$. Then $\overrightarrow{MN} = \overrightarrow{MB}+\overrightarrow{BN} = (1-k)\overrightarrow{AB} + k\overrightarrow{BC}$ and $\overrightarrow{SR} = \overrightarrow{SD}+\overrightarrow{DR} = k\overrightarrow{AD} + (1-k)\overrightarrow{DC} = k\overrightarrow{BC} + (1-k)\overrightarrow{AB}$. Therefore $\overrightarrow{MN} = \overrightarrow{SR}$; that is, two opposite sides of the quadrilateral $MNRS$ are equal and parallel. Hence $MNRS$ is a parallelogram.

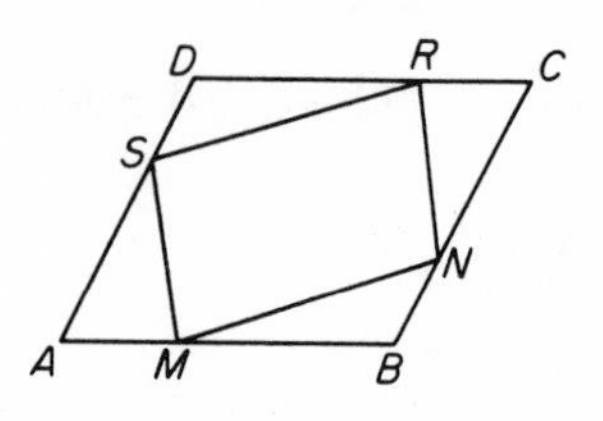

1-5 Linear Dependence of Vectors

1. (a) $\overrightarrow{OA}$; (b) $-\frac{1}{2}\overrightarrow{OC}$; (c) $\overrightarrow{OA}$. **3.** (a) $-2\overrightarrow{OA}$; (b) $\overrightarrow{OC}$; (c) $-2\overrightarrow{OA}$.

5. (a) $-\overrightarrow{OA} - \overrightarrow{OB}$; (b) $-\overrightarrow{OB} + \frac{1}{2}\overrightarrow{OC}$; (c) $5\overrightarrow{OA} - 2\overrightarrow{OD}$.

7. (a) $-\overrightarrow{OA} + \overrightarrow{OB}$; (b) $\overrightarrow{OB} + \frac{1}{2}\overrightarrow{OC}$; (c) $-7\overrightarrow{OA} + 2\overrightarrow{OD}$.

9. $\overrightarrow{OM} = \frac{1}{2}\overrightarrow{OA} + \frac{1}{2}\overrightarrow{OB}$. By Theorem 1-9, M is the mid-point of line segment AB.

11. $\overrightarrow{AD} = \overrightarrow{AB} + \frac{2}{5}\overrightarrow{BC} = \overrightarrow{AB} + \frac{2}{5}(\overrightarrow{AC} - \overrightarrow{AB}) = \frac{3}{5}\overrightarrow{AB} + \frac{2}{5}\overrightarrow{AC}$;
$3/5 + 2/5 = 1$. Then D, B, and C are collinear by Theorem 1-9.

13. Any two nonzero, nonparallel vectors of the form $m\vec{a} + n\vec{b}$ may be used; for example, $\vec{a} - \vec{b}$ and $\vec{a} + \vec{b}$.

15. Let $\vec{b}$ be a linear function of $\overrightarrow{a_1}, \overrightarrow{a_2}, \ldots, \overrightarrow{a_n}$. Assume that

$$\vec{b} = m_1\overrightarrow{a_1} + m_2\overrightarrow{a_2} + \cdots + m_n\overrightarrow{a_n} = k_1\overrightarrow{a_1} + k_2\overrightarrow{a_2} + \cdots + k_n\overrightarrow{a_n}.$$

Then

$$(m_1 - k_1)\overrightarrow{a_1} + (m_2 - k_2)\overrightarrow{a_2} + \cdots + (m_n - k_n)\overrightarrow{a_n} = \vec{0}.$$

Since $\overrightarrow{a_1}, \overrightarrow{a_2}, \ldots, \overrightarrow{a_n}$ are linearly independent vectors, then $m_1 - k_1 = m_2 - k_2 = \ldots = m_n - k_n = 0$ and $m_i = k_i$ for $i = 1, 2, \ldots, n$. Hence the two representations of $\vec{b}$ are identical.

1-6 Applications of Linear Dependence

1. Let $ABCD$ be any parallelogram. Let M be a point which divides sides BC in the ratio 1 to n and P be the point of intersection of line segment AM and diagonal BD. Then, by Theorem 1-9,

$$\begin{aligned}\overrightarrow{AM} &= \frac{n}{n+1}\overrightarrow{AB} + \frac{1}{n+1}\overrightarrow{AC} \\ &= \frac{n}{n+1}\overrightarrow{AB} + \frac{1}{n+1}(\overrightarrow{AD} + \overrightarrow{AB}) \\ &= \overrightarrow{AB} + \frac{1}{n+1}\overrightarrow{AD},\end{aligned}$$

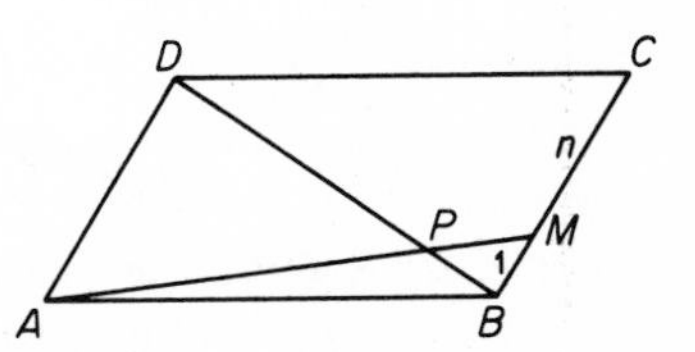

and

$$\overrightarrow{AP} = k\overrightarrow{AM} = k\overrightarrow{AB} + \frac{k}{n+1}\overrightarrow{AD}.$$

Since B, P, and D are collinear, $k + \{k/(n+1)\} = 1$, and $k = (n+1)/(n+2)$. Hence $\overrightarrow{AP} = \{(n+1)/(n+2)\}\overrightarrow{AB} + \{1/(n+2)\}\overrightarrow{AD}$; that is, P divides diagonal BD in the ratio 1 to $n+1$. If we let M be a point which divides side CB in the ratio 1 to n, then, in a similar manner, it follows that P divides diagonal BD in the ratio n to $n+1$.

3. Let ABC be any triangle with centroid at P and M the mid-point of side BC. Let O be any reference point in space. Then, by Theorem 1-9,

$$\begin{aligned}\overrightarrow{OP} &= \tfrac{1}{3}\overrightarrow{OA} + \tfrac{2}{3}\overrightarrow{OM} \\ &= \tfrac{1}{3}\overrightarrow{OA} + \tfrac{2}{3}(\tfrac{1}{2}\overrightarrow{OB} + \tfrac{1}{2}\overrightarrow{OC}) \\ &= \tfrac{1}{3}(\overrightarrow{OA} + \overrightarrow{OB} + \overrightarrow{OC}).\end{aligned}$$

5. Let $ABCD$ be any quadrilateral with M, N, R, and S mid-points of sides AB, BC, CD, and DA, respectively. Let O be any reference point. Then $\overrightarrow{OM} = \tfrac{1}{2}\overrightarrow{OA} + \tfrac{1}{2}\overrightarrow{OB}$; $\overrightarrow{ON} = \tfrac{1}{2}\overrightarrow{OB} + \tfrac{1}{2}\overrightarrow{OC}$; $\overrightarrow{OR} = \tfrac{1}{2}\overrightarrow{OC} + \tfrac{1}{2}\overrightarrow{OD}$; and $\overrightarrow{OS} = \tfrac{1}{2}\overrightarrow{OD} + \tfrac{1}{2}\overrightarrow{OA}$. Now,

$$\begin{aligned}\overrightarrow{MN} &= \overrightarrow{ON} - \overrightarrow{OM} = \tfrac{1}{2}(\overrightarrow{OC} - \overrightarrow{OA}) = \tfrac{1}{2}\overrightarrow{AC}; \\ \overrightarrow{SR} &= \overrightarrow{OR} - \overrightarrow{OS} = \tfrac{1}{2}(\overrightarrow{OC} - \overrightarrow{OA}) = \tfrac{1}{2}\overrightarrow{AC}.\end{aligned}$$

Hence $\overrightarrow{MN} = \overrightarrow{SR}$; that is, $\overrightarrow{MN}$ is parallel to $\overrightarrow{SR}$ and $|\overrightarrow{MN}| = |\overrightarrow{SR}|$. Since two opposite sides, MN and SR, of the quadrilateral $MNRS$ are equal and parallel, the quadrilateral is a parallelogram.

7. Let $ABCD$ be any tetrahedron. Let M, N, R, and S be the mid-points of edges AB, CD, BD, and AC, respectively. Let P and P' be the mid-points of line segments MN and RS, respectively. If O is any reference point, then

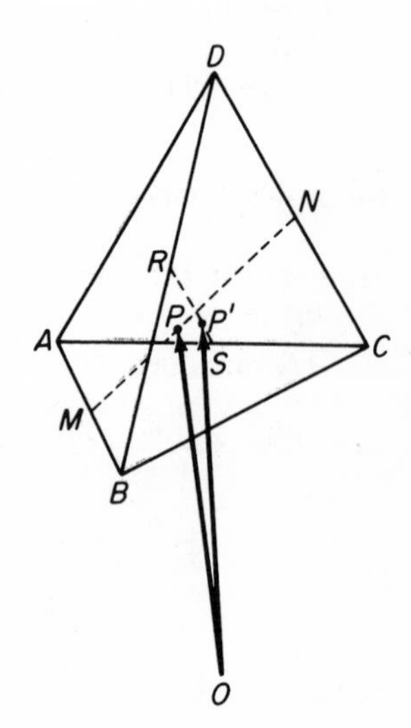

$$\begin{aligned}\overrightarrow{OP} &= \tfrac{1}{2}\overrightarrow{OM} + \tfrac{1}{2}\overrightarrow{ON} \\ &= \tfrac{1}{2}(\tfrac{1}{2}\overrightarrow{OA} + \tfrac{1}{2}\overrightarrow{OB}) + \tfrac{1}{2}(\tfrac{1}{2}\overrightarrow{OC} + \tfrac{1}{2}\overrightarrow{OD}) \\ &= \tfrac{1}{4}(\overrightarrow{OA} + \overrightarrow{OB} + \overrightarrow{OC} + \overrightarrow{OD});\end{aligned}$$

$$\begin{aligned}\overrightarrow{OP'} &= \tfrac{1}{2}\overrightarrow{OR} + \tfrac{1}{2}\overrightarrow{OS} \\ &= \tfrac{1}{2}(\tfrac{1}{2}\overrightarrow{OB} + \tfrac{1}{2}\overrightarrow{OD}) + \tfrac{1}{2}(\tfrac{1}{2}\overrightarrow{OA} + \tfrac{1}{2}\overrightarrow{OC}) \\ &= \tfrac{1}{4}(\overrightarrow{OA} + \overrightarrow{OB} + \overrightarrow{OC} + \overrightarrow{OD}).\end{aligned}$$

Since $\overrightarrow{OP} = \overrightarrow{OP'}$, the points P and P' coincide; that is, the line segments bisect each other.

9. Let $ABCDE$ be any regular pentagon with center at O. Let $\vec{r}_1, \vec{r}_2, \ldots, \vec{r}_5$ be vectors drawn from the center to vertices $A, B, \ldots, E$, respectively. Let $\vec{a}_1, \vec{a}_2, \ldots, \vec{a}_5$ be vectors drawn from the center to the mid-points of sides $CD, DE, \ldots, BC$, respectively. Then,

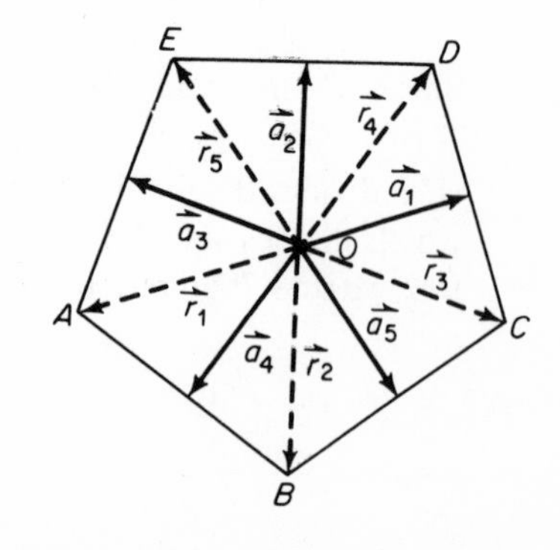

$$\begin{aligned}\vec{a}_1 &= \tfrac{1}{2}\vec{r}_3 + \tfrac{1}{2}\vec{r}_4, \\ \vec{a}_2 &= \tfrac{1}{2}\vec{r}_4 + \tfrac{1}{2}\vec{r}_5,\end{aligned}$$

$$\vdots \qquad \vdots$$

$$\overrightarrow{a_5} = \tfrac{1}{2}\overrightarrow{r_2} + \tfrac{1}{2}\overrightarrow{r_3}.$$

Therefore, $\overrightarrow{a_1} + \overrightarrow{a_2} + \cdots + \overrightarrow{a_5} = \overrightarrow{r_1} + \overrightarrow{r_2} + \cdots + \overrightarrow{r_5}$. Now, $\overrightarrow{a_1} = m\overrightarrow{r_1}$, $\overrightarrow{a_2} = m\overrightarrow{r_2}, \ldots, \overrightarrow{a_5} = m\overrightarrow{r_5}$. Hence, $m(\overrightarrow{r_1} + \overrightarrow{r_2} + \cdots + \overrightarrow{r_5}) = \overrightarrow{r_1} + \overrightarrow{r_2} + \cdots + \overrightarrow{r_5}$, $(m-1)(\overrightarrow{r_1} + \overrightarrow{r_2} + \cdots + \overrightarrow{r_5}) = \vec{0}$. Since $m \neq 1$, then $\overrightarrow{r_1} + \overrightarrow{r_2} + \cdots + \overrightarrow{r_5} = \vec{0}$.

11. Associate vectors $\vec{b}$ and $\vec{c}$ with sides AC and AB, respectively. Let line AP be determined by the external bisector of angle A, where P lies on line BC. Now,

$$\overrightarrow{AP} = k\left(\frac{\vec{b}}{|\vec{b}|} - \frac{\vec{c}}{|\vec{c}|}\right) = k\left(\frac{|\vec{c}|\vec{b} - |\vec{b}|\vec{c}}{|\vec{b}||\vec{c}|}\right),$$

where k is such that the sum of the coefficients of $\vec{b}$ and $\vec{c}$ is one. Then

$$k = \frac{|\vec{b}||\vec{c}|}{|\vec{c}| - |\vec{b}|},$$

and

$$\overrightarrow{AP} = \frac{|\vec{c}|}{|\vec{c}| - |\vec{b}|}\vec{b} - \frac{|\vec{b}|}{|\vec{c}| - |\vec{b}|}\vec{c}.$$

Hence,

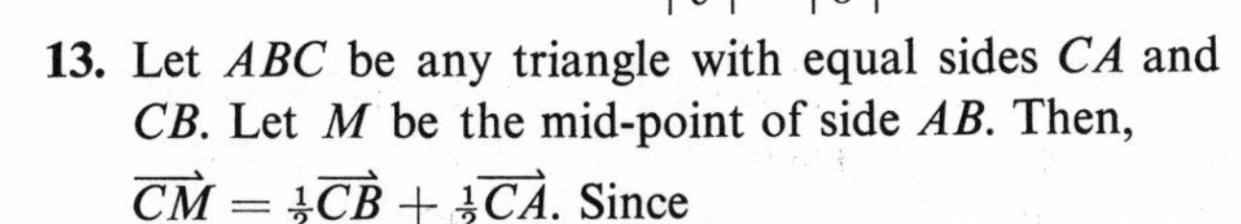

$$\frac{|\overrightarrow{BP}|}{|\overrightarrow{PC}|} = \frac{\dfrac{|\vec{c}|}{|\vec{c}| - |\vec{b}|}}{\dfrac{|\vec{b}|}{|\vec{c}| - |\vec{b}|}} = \frac{|\vec{c}|}{|\vec{b}|} = \frac{|\overrightarrow{AB}|}{|\overrightarrow{AC}|}.$$

13. Let ABC be any triangle with equal sides CA and CB. Let M be the mid-point of side AB. Then, $\overrightarrow{CM} = \frac{1}{2}\overrightarrow{CB} + \frac{1}{2}\overrightarrow{CA}$. Since $|\overrightarrow{CB}| = |\overrightarrow{CA}|$, then

$$\overrightarrow{CM} = k\left(\frac{\overrightarrow{CB}}{|\overrightarrow{CB}|} + \frac{\overrightarrow{CA}}{|\overrightarrow{CA}|}\right).$$

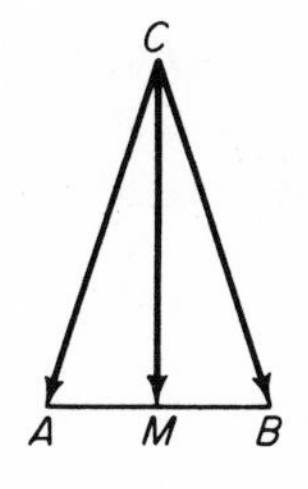

Hence, the line segment CM lies along the bisector of angle C.

1-7 Position Vectors

1. (a) $2\vec{i} + 2\vec{j} + \vec{k}$; (b) 3; (c) $\frac{2}{3}\vec{i} + \frac{2}{3}\vec{j} + \frac{1}{3}\vec{k}$.

3. (a) $3\vec{i}$; (b) 3; (c) $\vec{i}$.

5. yz-plane.

7. A plane parallel to and three units from the yz-plane along the positive x-axis.

9. A unit sphere with center at the origin.

11. **(a)** $|z|$; **(b)** $\sqrt{y^2 + z^2}$.

13. M, N, and P are not collinear.

15. **(a)** $(\frac{11}{2}, 4, \frac{19}{2})$; **(b)** $(5, 3, 11)$; **(c)** $(13, 19, -13)$.

Chapter 2—Products of Vectors

2-1 The Scalar Product

1. $3; \frac{2}{3}\vec{i} + \frac{2}{3}\vec{j} + \frac{1}{3}\vec{k}$.

3. $\frac{13}{5}$.

5. **(a)** Since $|\cos(\vec{r_1}, \vec{r_2})| \leq 1$, $|\vec{r_1}\cdot\vec{r_2}| \leq |\vec{r_1}||\vec{r_2}|$; **(b)** $\cos(\vec{r_1}, \vec{r_2}) = 1$, that is, $\vec{r_1}$ has the same direction as $\vec{r_2}$; **(c)** $\cos(\vec{r_1}, \vec{r_2}) = -1$, that is, $\vec{r_1}$ has an opposite direction to $\vec{r_2}$.

7. $\dfrac{\sqrt{3}}{3}$.

9. By Theorem 2-4, $\angle ABC$ is a right angle since $\overrightarrow{BA}\cdot\overrightarrow{BC} = 0$; $|\overrightarrow{BA}| = |\overrightarrow{BC}|$; hence, $\triangle ABC$ is a right isosceles triangle.

11. By Theorem 2-2, $\vec{a}\cdot\vec{a} = |\vec{a}|^2$. If $\vec{a}\cdot\vec{a} = 0$, then $|\vec{a}| = 0$. If $|\vec{a}| = 0$, then $\vec{a}\cdot\vec{a} = 0^2 = 0$.

13. $\overrightarrow{AB} = -\vec{i} + \vec{j}$; $\overrightarrow{AC} = -\vec{i} + \vec{k}$; $\dfrac{\overrightarrow{AB}\cdot\overrightarrow{AC}}{|\overrightarrow{AC}|} = \dfrac{\sqrt{2}}{2}$.

2-2 Applications of the Scalar Product

1. Let $ABCD$ be a rhombus. Let $\vec{a}$ and $\vec{b}$ be associated with the adjacent sides AB and BC, respectively. Then $\vec{a} + \vec{b}$ and $\vec{a} - \vec{b}$ are vectors associated with the diagonals. By Theorems 2-5, 2-1, and 2-2,

$$\begin{aligned}(\vec{a} + \vec{b})\cdot(\vec{a} - \vec{b}) &= (\vec{a} + \vec{b})\cdot\vec{a} - (\vec{a} + \vec{b})\cdot\vec{b} \\ &= \vec{a}\cdot\vec{a} + \vec{b}\cdot\vec{a} - \vec{a}\cdot\vec{b} - \vec{b}\cdot\vec{b} \\ &= \vec{a}\cdot\vec{a} - \vec{b}\cdot\vec{b} \\ &= |\vec{a}|^2 - |\vec{b}|^2 \\ &= 0. \qquad (\text{since } |\vec{a}| = |\vec{b}|)\end{aligned}$$

Since $|\vec{a} + \vec{b}| \neq 0$ and $|\vec{a} - \vec{b}| \neq 0$, then by Theorem 2-4 $(\vec{a} + \vec{b}) \perp (\vec{a} - \vec{b})$; that is, the diagonals of a rhombus are perpendicular.

3. Let ABC be any right triangle with right angle at C. If M is the mid-point of the hypotenuse AB, then $\overrightarrow{CM} = \frac{1}{2}(\overrightarrow{CA} + \overrightarrow{CB})$, and

$$\begin{aligned}\overrightarrow{CM}\cdot\overrightarrow{CM} &= \tfrac{1}{2}(\overrightarrow{CA} + \overrightarrow{CB})\cdot\tfrac{1}{2}(\overrightarrow{CA} + \overrightarrow{CB})\\ &= \tfrac{1}{4}(\overrightarrow{CA}\cdot\overrightarrow{CA} + \overrightarrow{CB}\cdot\overrightarrow{CA} + \overrightarrow{CA}\cdot\overrightarrow{CB} + \overrightarrow{CB}\cdot\overrightarrow{CB})\\ &= \tfrac{1}{4}(\overrightarrow{CA}\cdot\overrightarrow{CA} + \overrightarrow{CB}\cdot\overrightarrow{CB})\\ &\quad \text{(since } \overrightarrow{CB}\cdot\overrightarrow{CA} = \overrightarrow{CA}\cdot\overrightarrow{CB} = 0)\\ &= \tfrac{1}{4}(|\overrightarrow{CA}|^2 + |\overrightarrow{CB}|^2)\\ &= \tfrac{1}{4}|\overrightarrow{AB}|^2.\\ &\quad \text{(by the Pythagorean Theorem)}\end{aligned}$$

Hence, $|\overrightarrow{CM}|^2 = \frac{1}{4}|\overrightarrow{AB}|^2$ and $|\overrightarrow{CM}| = \frac{1}{2}|\overrightarrow{AB}|$; that is, the median to the hypotenuse is equal to one-half the hypotenuse.

5. Let $ABCD$ be any quadrilateral with M, N, R, and S mid-points of sides AB, BC, CD, and DA, respectively. Since

$$\begin{aligned}\overrightarrow{MR} &= \overrightarrow{MB} + \overrightarrow{BC} + \overrightarrow{CR}\\ &= \tfrac{1}{2}\overrightarrow{AB} + \overrightarrow{BC} + \tfrac{1}{2}\overrightarrow{CD}\end{aligned}$$

and

$$\begin{aligned}\overrightarrow{SN} &= \overrightarrow{SA} + \overrightarrow{AB} + \overrightarrow{BN}\\ &= \tfrac{1}{2}\overrightarrow{DA} + \overrightarrow{AB} + \tfrac{1}{2}\overrightarrow{BC},\end{aligned}$$

then

$$\begin{aligned}2\overrightarrow{MR} &= \overrightarrow{AB} + 2\overrightarrow{BC} + \overrightarrow{CD}\\ &= (\overrightarrow{AB} + \overrightarrow{BC}) + (\overrightarrow{BC} + \overrightarrow{CD})\\ &= \overrightarrow{AC} + \overrightarrow{BD}\end{aligned}$$

and

$$\begin{aligned}2\overrightarrow{SN} &= \overrightarrow{DA} + 2\overrightarrow{AB} + \overrightarrow{BC}\\ &= (\overrightarrow{DA} + \overrightarrow{AB}) + (\overrightarrow{AB} + \overrightarrow{BC})\\ &= \overrightarrow{DB} + \overrightarrow{AC}\\ &= \overrightarrow{AC} - \overrightarrow{BD}.\end{aligned}$$

Now

$$\begin{aligned}4|\overrightarrow{MR}|^2 = 2\overrightarrow{MR}\cdot 2\overrightarrow{MR} &= (\overrightarrow{AC} + \overrightarrow{BD})\cdot(\overrightarrow{AC} + \overrightarrow{BD})\\ &= |\overrightarrow{AC}|^2 + |\overrightarrow{BD}|^2 + 2\overrightarrow{AC}\cdot\overrightarrow{BD}\end{aligned}$$

and

$$\begin{aligned}4|\overrightarrow{SN}|^2 = 2\overrightarrow{SN}\cdot 2\overrightarrow{SN} &= (\overrightarrow{AC} - \overrightarrow{BD})\cdot(\overrightarrow{AC} - \overrightarrow{BD})\\ &= |\overrightarrow{AC}|^2 + |\overrightarrow{BD}|^2 - 2\overrightarrow{AC}\cdot\overrightarrow{BD}.\end{aligned}$$

Hence

$$4|\overrightarrow{MR}|^2 + 4|\overrightarrow{SN}|^2 = 2|\overrightarrow{AC}|^2 + 2|\overrightarrow{BD}|^2;$$

that is,

$$2(|\overrightarrow{MR}|^2 + |\overrightarrow{SN}|^2) = |\overrightarrow{AC}|^2 + |\overrightarrow{BD}|^2.$$

7. Let $\vec{a}$ and $\vec{b}$ be unit position vectors on a cartesian coordinate plane forming angles θ and $-\phi$, respectively, with the positive half of the x-axis. Then $\vec{a} = \cos\theta\vec{i} + \sin\theta\vec{j}$ and $\vec{b} = \cos(-\phi)\vec{i} + \sin(-\phi)\vec{j} = \cos\phi\vec{i} - \sin\phi\vec{j}$. By Definition 2-1, $\vec{a}\cdot\vec{b} = |\vec{a}||\vec{b}|\cos(\vec{a}, \vec{b}) = |\vec{a}||\vec{b}| \cos[-(\theta + \phi)] = |\vec{a}||\vec{b}| \cos(\theta + \phi) = \cos(\theta + \phi)$. By the properties of the scalar product of the unit position vectors,

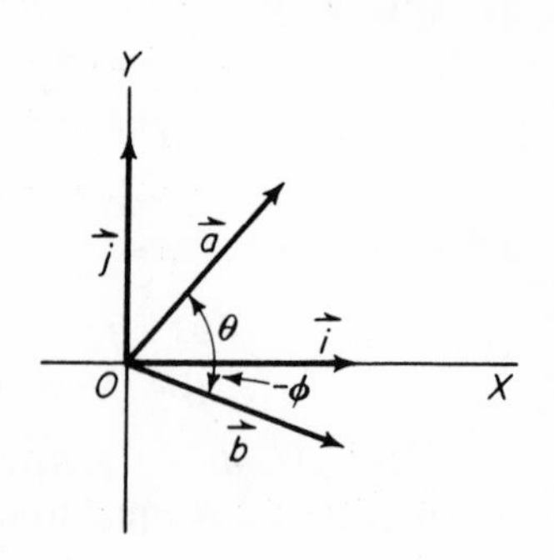

$$\vec{a}\cdot\vec{b} = \cos\theta\cos\phi - \sin\theta\sin\phi.$$

Hence $\cos(\theta + \phi) = \cos\theta\cos\phi - \sin\theta\sin\phi$.

9. Let ABC be any triangle. Then

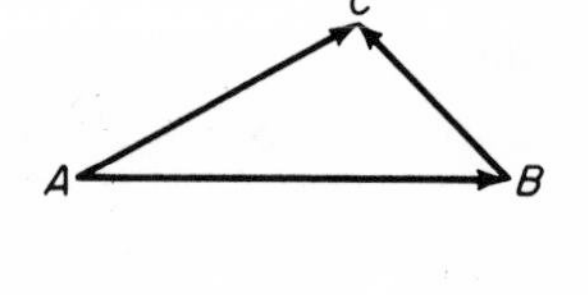

$$\overrightarrow{AC} = \overrightarrow{AB} + \overrightarrow{BC}$$

$$\overrightarrow{AB}\cdot\overrightarrow{AC} = \overrightarrow{AB}\cdot(\overrightarrow{AB} + \overrightarrow{BC})$$

$$= \overrightarrow{AB}\cdot\overrightarrow{AB} + \overrightarrow{AB}\cdot\overrightarrow{BC};$$

$$|\overrightarrow{AB}||\overrightarrow{AC}|\cos A = |\overrightarrow{AB}|\,|\overrightarrow{AB}| + |\overrightarrow{AB}||\overrightarrow{BC}|\cos(180° - B)$$

$$|\overrightarrow{AC}|\cos A = |\overrightarrow{AB}| - |\overrightarrow{BC}|\cos B.$$

Hence

$$|\overrightarrow{AB}| = |\overrightarrow{AC}|\cos A + |\overrightarrow{BC}|\cos B.$$

2-3 Circles and Lines on a Coordinate Plane

1. $x^2 + y^2 - 2x + 6y - 6 = 0.$

3. 2 units.

5. $\vec{r} = m\vec{b}.$

7. $\vec{r} = \vec{a} + m\vec{b}.$

9. $r = \dfrac{|c|}{\sqrt{a^2 + b^2}}.$

2-4 Translation and Rotation

1. (2, 5).

3. (−5, 3).

5. $x' = x\cos\theta + y\sin\theta$; $y' = -x\sin\theta + y\cos\theta.$

7. $\left(\dfrac{3\sqrt{3}}{2}, \dfrac{1}{2}\right).$

9. $(2\sqrt{2}, 0).$

11. $x'^2 - 2y' = 0.$

13. $2x' + 5 = 0.$

15. $x'^2 + 4y'^2 - 4 = 0.$

17. $\left(\frac{4\sqrt{3}-1}{2}, \frac{10-3\sqrt{3}}{2}\right)$.

19. $\theta = 45°$.

21. $B' = 0$ if $B(\cos^2\theta - \sin^2\theta) - 2(A-C)\sin\theta\cos\theta = 0$; $B\cos 2\theta - (A-C)\sin 2\theta = 0$; $B\cos 2\theta = (A-C)\sin 2\theta$; $\tan 2\theta = B/(A-C)$; $\theta = \frac{1}{2}\arctan B/(A-C)$.

2-5 Orthogonal Bases

1. -1 and -2.

3. $\frac{\sqrt{2}}{2}\vec{i} + \frac{\sqrt{2}}{2}\vec{k}$ and $-\frac{\sqrt{3}}{3}\vec{i} + \frac{\sqrt{3}}{3}\vec{j} + \frac{\sqrt{3}}{3}\vec{k}$.

There are also other correct answers.

2-6 The Vector Product

1. $3\vec{i} \times (\vec{i} + 2\vec{j}) = 6\vec{k}$ and $3\vec{i} \times 2\vec{j} = 6\vec{k}$.

3.
$$\begin{vmatrix} a_1 & b_1 & \vec{i} \\ a_2 & b_2 & \vec{j} \\ a_3 & b_3 & \vec{k} \end{vmatrix} = a_1\begin{vmatrix} b_2 & \vec{j} \\ b_3 & \vec{k} \end{vmatrix} + b_1\begin{vmatrix} \vec{j} & a_2 \\ \vec{k} & a_3 \end{vmatrix} + \vec{i}\begin{vmatrix} a_2 & b_2 \\ a_3 & b_3 \end{vmatrix}$$
$$= a_1b_2\vec{k} - a_1b_3\vec{j} + b_1a_3\vec{j} - b_1a_2\vec{k} + a_2b_3\vec{i} - a_3b_2\vec{i}$$
$$= (a_2b_3 - a_3b_2)\vec{i} + (a_3b_1 - a_1b_3)\vec{j} + (a_1b_2 - a_2b_1)\vec{k}$$
$$= \vec{a} \times \vec{b}.$$

5. $\frac{\vec{a} \times \vec{b}}{|\vec{a} \times \vec{b}|} = \frac{\sqrt{3}}{3}\vec{i} - \frac{\sqrt{3}}{3}\vec{j} - \frac{\sqrt{3}}{3}\vec{k}$.

7. $A = \frac{1}{2}|\vec{a} \times \vec{b}| = \sqrt{61}$ (square units).

9. $\vec{a} \times \vec{b} = \vec{a} \times (-\vec{a} - \vec{c}) = -\vec{a} \times \vec{c} = \vec{c} \times \vec{a}$;
$\vec{c} \times \vec{a} = \vec{c} \times (-\vec{b} - \vec{c}) = \vec{c} \times (-\vec{b}) = \vec{b} \times \vec{c}$.

2-7 Applications of the Vector Product

1. 1 square unit.

3. By Theorem 2-15, $\vec{b} \times \vec{a} = (\sin\theta\cos\phi + \cos\theta\sin\phi)\vec{k}$. By Definition 2-2, $\vec{b} \times \vec{a} = |\vec{b}||\vec{a}|\sin[\theta - (-\phi)]\vec{k} = \sin(\theta + \phi)\vec{k}$. Hence, $\sin(\theta + \phi) = \sin\theta\cos\phi + \cos\theta\sin\phi$.

5. The law of reflection of light states that when a ray of light strikes a plane mirror and is reflected, the incident ray and the reflected ray each form equal angles with the surface of the mirror. Therefore $\vec{a} \times \vec{n} = \vec{b} \times \vec{n}$ represents a vector form of the law of reflection of light, since $\sin(\vec{a}, \vec{n}) = \sin(\vec{b}, \vec{n})$.

7. The area of triangle ABC equals $\frac{1}{2}|\overrightarrow{AB} \times \overrightarrow{AC}|$, and the area of triangle HJG equals $\frac{1}{2}|\overrightarrow{JG} \times \overrightarrow{JH}|$. Now,

$$\begin{aligned}
\overrightarrow{JG} \times \overrightarrow{JH} &= \tfrac{3}{7}\overrightarrow{AD} \times \tfrac{3}{7}\overrightarrow{FC} \\
&= \tfrac{3}{7}(\overrightarrow{AB} + \overrightarrow{BD}) \times \tfrac{3}{7}(\overrightarrow{FA} + \overrightarrow{AC}) \\
&= \tfrac{3}{7}(\overrightarrow{AB} + \tfrac{1}{3}\overrightarrow{BC}) \times \tfrac{3}{7}(-\tfrac{1}{3}\overrightarrow{AB} + \overrightarrow{AC}) \\
&= (\tfrac{3}{7}\overrightarrow{AB} + \tfrac{1}{7}\overrightarrow{BC}) \times (-\tfrac{1}{7}\overrightarrow{AB} + \tfrac{3}{7}\overrightarrow{AC}) \\
&= (\tfrac{3}{7}\overrightarrow{AB} + \tfrac{1}{7}\overrightarrow{AC} - \tfrac{1}{7}\overrightarrow{AB}) \times (-\tfrac{1}{7}\overrightarrow{AB} + \tfrac{3}{7}\overrightarrow{AC}) \\
&= (\tfrac{2}{7}\overrightarrow{AB} + \tfrac{1}{7}\overrightarrow{AC}) \times (-\tfrac{1}{7}\overrightarrow{AB} + \tfrac{3}{7}\overrightarrow{AC}) \\
&= \tfrac{6}{49}(\overrightarrow{AB} \times \overrightarrow{AC}) - \tfrac{1}{49}(\overrightarrow{AC} \times \overrightarrow{AB}) \\
&= \tfrac{6}{49}(\overrightarrow{AB} \times \overrightarrow{AC}) + \tfrac{1}{49}(\overrightarrow{AB} \times \overrightarrow{AC}) \\
&= \tfrac{1}{7}(\overrightarrow{AB} \times \overrightarrow{AC}).
\end{aligned}$$

Hence the area of triangle HJG is one-seventh the area of triangle ABC.

2-8 The Scalar Triple Product

1. **(a)** 1; **(b)** −1; **(c)** 0.
3. 2 cubic units.
5. 6 cubic units.
7. $\vec{a}\cdot(\vec{b} \times \vec{c}) = (2\vec{i} + 3\vec{j} - 4\vec{k})\cdot(-3\vec{i} - \vec{j} + 2\vec{k}) = -17$; $(\vec{a} \times \vec{b})\cdot\vec{c} = (-\vec{i} - 6\vec{j} - 5\vec{k})\cdot(\vec{i} + \vec{j} + 2\vec{k}) = -17$.
9. No.

2-9 The Vector Triple Product

1. **(a)** $\vec{0}$; **(b)** $\vec{j}$; **(c)** $\vec{j}$.
3. By (2-47),

$$\begin{aligned}
\vec{a} \times (\vec{b} \times \vec{c}) &= (\vec{a}\cdot\vec{c})\vec{b} - (\vec{a}\cdot\vec{b})\vec{c}; \\
\vec{b} \times (\vec{c} \times \vec{a}) &= (\vec{b}\cdot\vec{a})\vec{c} - (\vec{b}\cdot\vec{c})\vec{a}; \\
\vec{c} \times (\vec{a} \times \vec{b}) &= (\vec{c}\cdot\vec{b})\vec{a} - (\vec{c}\cdot\vec{a})\vec{b}.
\end{aligned}$$

Hence, $\vec{a} \times (\vec{b} \times \vec{c}) + \vec{b} \times (\vec{c} \times \vec{a}) + \vec{c} \times (\vec{a} \times \vec{b}) = \vec{0}$.

2-10 Quadruple Products

1. By (2-50), $(\vec{a} \times \vec{b})\cdot(\vec{b} \times \vec{c}) \times (\vec{c} \times \vec{a})$

$$= \begin{vmatrix} \vec{a}\cdot(\vec{b} \times \vec{c}) & \vec{a}\cdot(\vec{c} \times \vec{a}) \\ \vec{b}\cdot(\vec{b} \times \vec{c}) & \vec{b}\cdot(\vec{c} \times \vec{a}) \end{vmatrix}$$

$$= \begin{vmatrix} (\vec{a}\vec{b}\vec{c}) & \vec{0} \\ \vec{0} & (\vec{a}\vec{b}\vec{c}) \end{vmatrix} = (\vec{a}\vec{b}\vec{c})^2.$$

3. $(\vec{a} \times \vec{b})\cdot(\vec{c} \times \vec{d}) \times (\vec{e} \times \vec{f}) = (\vec{c} \times \vec{d})\cdot(\vec{e} \times \vec{f}) \times (\vec{a} \times \vec{b})$.
Then, by (2-50),

$$(\vec{c} \times \vec{d})\cdot(\vec{e} \times \vec{f}) \times (\vec{a} \times \vec{b}) = \begin{vmatrix} \vec{c}\cdot(\vec{e} \times \vec{f}) & \vec{c}\cdot(\vec{a} \times \vec{b}) \\ \vec{d}\cdot(\vec{e} \times \vec{f}) & \vec{d}\cdot(\vec{a} \times \vec{b}) \end{vmatrix}$$
$$= (\vec{a}\vec{b}\vec{d})(\vec{c}\vec{e}\vec{f}) - (\vec{a}\vec{b}\vec{c})(\vec{d}\vec{e}\vec{f}).$$

5. $(\vec{a} \times \vec{b})\cdot(\vec{c} \times \vec{d}) = (4\vec{i} + 8\vec{j} + 4\vec{k})\cdot(-3\vec{i} + \vec{j} - 2\vec{k}) = -12;$

$$\begin{vmatrix} \vec{a}\cdot\vec{c} & \vec{a}\cdot\vec{d} \\ \vec{b}\cdot\vec{c} & \vec{b}\cdot\vec{d} \end{vmatrix} = \begin{vmatrix} -3 & 0 \\ 2 & 4 \end{vmatrix} = -12.$$

2-11 Quaternions

1. **(a)** $(2, 5, 0, 2)$; **(b)** $(7, 13, -3, 9)$; **(c)** $(6, 3, 0, -9)$.

3. $\dfrac{a - bi - cj - dk}{a^2 + b^2 + c^2 + d^2}$.

5. If $a + bi \longleftrightarrow a + bi + 0j + 0k$ and
$c + di \longleftrightarrow c + di + 0j + 0k$, then $(a + bi) + (c + di)$
$= (a + c) + (b + d)i \longleftrightarrow (a + bi + 0j + 0k) + (c + di + 0j + 0k)$
$= (a + c) + (b + d)i + 0j + 0k$, and $(a + bi)(c + di)$
$= (ac - bd) + (ad + bc)i \longleftrightarrow (a + bi + 0j + 0k)(c + di + 0j + 0k)$
$= (ac - bd) + (ad + bc)i + 0j + 0k$.

7. Let $x = a + bi + cj + dk$ and $y = e + fi + gj + hk$. Then

$$\begin{aligned} xy &= (ae - bf - cg - dh) + (af + be + ch - dg)i \\ &\quad + (ag + ce + df - bh)j + (ah + de + bg - cf)k; \\ (xy)^* &= (ae - bf - cg - dh) - (af + be + ch - dg)i \\ &\quad - (ag + ce + df - bh)j - (ah + de + bg - cf)k; \\ y^* &= e - fi - gj - hk; \qquad x^* = a - bi - cj - dk; \\ y^*x^* &= (ae - bf - cg - dh) - (af + be + ch - dg)i \\ &\quad - (ag + ce + df - bh)j - (ah + de + bg - cf)k; \\ (xy)^* &= y^*x^*. \end{aligned}$$

Chapter 3—Planes and Lines in Space

3-1 Direction Cosines and Numbers

1. $(\frac{3}{13}: \frac{12}{13}: -\frac{4}{13})$.

3. $(3k: 12k: -4k)$, where k is any real number such that $k > 0$.

5. (b).

7. **(a)** 45° or 135°; **(b)** 45°, 135°, 225°, or 315°.

9. $\left(\dfrac{\sqrt{10}}{10}: 0: -\dfrac{3\sqrt{10}}{10}\right)$ or $\left(-\dfrac{\sqrt{10}}{10}: 0: \dfrac{3\sqrt{10}}{10}\right)$.

11. Any three points of the form $(2 + 3k, 1 - k, -4 + k)$, where k is any real number such that $k \neq 0$.

13. $60°$.

15. $\frac{\sqrt{3}}{3}$.

3-2 Equation of a Plane

1. $3x - 2y + z - 14 = 0$.

3. $3x + 6y + z = 0$.

5. $x = 1 - 4m + 4n$; $y = 2 - n$; $z = 4m - n$.

7. **(a)** $2b + d = 0$; **(b)** $b = c$; **(c)** $a = b = c$; **(d)** $a = 2t$, $b = -t$, and $c = t$ for some real number $t \neq 0$; **(e)** $a = t$, $b = 3t$, and $c = 5t$ for some real number $t \neq 0$; **(f)** $d = 0$; **(g)** $2a - b + 4c + d = 0$; **(h)** $b = 0$; **(i)** $b = c = 0$; **(j)** $c = d = 0$.

9. $2x + 3y - 7z + 28 = 0$.

11. $\overrightarrow{OP} = \overrightarrow{OC} + m\overrightarrow{OA} + n\overrightarrow{OB}$ or $\overrightarrow{CP} \cdot \overrightarrow{OA} \times \overrightarrow{OB} = 0$.

3-3 Equation of a Sphere

1. $x^2 + y^2 + z^2 - 2x + 4y - 8z + 12 = 0$.

3. $x + y + 2z - 18 = 0$.

5. $x - 2 = 0$.

7. $x^2 + y^2 + z^2 - 4z - 1 = 0$.

9. $x - 1 = 0$.

3-4 Angle Between Two Planes

1. $45°$ and $135°$.

3. The planes are parallel since the nonzero vectors normal to the planes are parallel: $(3\vec{i} - 2\vec{j} + \vec{k}) \times (9\vec{i} - 6\vec{j} + 3\vec{k}) = \vec{0}$. An alternative proof may be given by showing that the same direction numbers $(3: -2: 1)$ may be used for a vector normal to each plane.

5. $45°$.

3-5 Distance Between a Point and a Plane

1. $2\sqrt{6}$ units.

3. 3 or -15.

5. 2 units.

7. -2.

9. $x^2 + y^2 + z^2 - 4x - 4y - 2z + 5 = 0$.

3-6 Equation of a Line

1. $x = 4 + 2m, \quad y = 5 - 3m, \quad z = 2 + m.$
3. $\dfrac{x-1}{3} = \dfrac{y-2}{1} = \dfrac{z}{-2}.$
5. $\dfrac{x}{3} = \dfrac{y}{5} = \dfrac{z}{-1}.$
7. $x = 4 - 3m, \quad y = 1, \quad z = 3 - m.$
9. $\dfrac{x-3}{3} = \dfrac{y+1}{5} = \dfrac{z-4}{2}.$
11. $(\frac{2}{3}\colon -\frac{2}{3}\colon \frac{1}{3})$ or $(-\frac{2}{3}\colon \frac{2}{3}\colon -\frac{1}{3})$.
13. $\left(0\colon \dfrac{\sqrt{2}}{2}\colon \dfrac{\sqrt{2}}{2}\right)$ or $\left(0\colon -\dfrac{\sqrt{2}}{2}\colon -\dfrac{\sqrt{2}}{2}\right).$
15. $(\frac{46}{5}, -\frac{13}{5}, 0)$.
17. $[(3\vec{i} - \vec{j}) \times (4\vec{i} - \vec{k})]\cdot[(\vec{j} + \vec{k}) \times (\vec{i} - \vec{j})] = (\vec{i} + 3\vec{j} + 4\vec{k})\cdot(\vec{i} + \vec{j} - \vec{k}) = 0.$
19. $5x - 2y + 11z = 0.$

3-7 Skew Lines

1. (a) 45°; (b) 90°.
3. The line determined by the planes $2x - 4y - 15z + 30 = 0$ and $16x + 17y + 27z - 89 = 0$.
5. $\begin{vmatrix} 1-(-2) & 3-4 & 3-(-2) \\ 1 & -1 & 2 \\ 2 & 0 & 3 \end{vmatrix} = 0.$

3-8 Distance Between a Point and a Line

1. $\dfrac{4\sqrt{61}}{7}$ units.
3. $\dfrac{\sqrt{6}}{3}s$ units.

Index